Brought to Book

Simon Bognor would never describe himself as 'bookish', in fact he believed the novel had died at the outbreak of World War I, so of course this hostile attitude made him the natural choice to head the Board of Trade's investigation into the publishing industry.

To further his knowledge of the book trade, Simon and Monica attend the sales conference of Big Books PLC. On the second morning Vernon Hemlock, creator of the publishing conglomerate, is found dead – compressed between the sliding shelves of his porno-graphic library.

Bognor, with his usual reluctance, agrees to represent the Board of Trade in the murder inquiry and loses no time in antagonising the local police. Suspects abound: Hemlock's widow, his mistress, his disaffected authors and his hated rival, Andover Strobe. But as the case progresses it soon becomes clear that there are far weightier matters involved and that the causes of Hemlock's death stretch beyond publishing to White-hall, Washington and Moscow.

As well as providing a satisfying and witty whodunit, Tim Heald gives his readers a bonus with a tongue-in-cheek look inside the publishing industry. *Brought to Book* is high entertainment.

BROUGHT TO BOOK

Tim Heald

MACMILLAN
LONDON

First published in 1988 by
MACMILLAN LONDON LIMITED
4 Little Essex Street London WC2R 3LF
and Basingstoke

Associated companies in Auckland, Delhi, Dublin,
Gaborone, Hamburg, Harare, Hong Kong, Johannesburg,
Kuala Lumpur, Lagos, Manzini, Melbourne, Mexico City,
Nairobi, New York, Singapore and Tokyo

British Library Cataloguing in Publication Data
Heald, Tim
  Brought to book.
  I. Title
823'914 [F]   PR6058.E167

ISBN 0-333-45876-1

Typeset by Columns, Reading

Printed and bound in the U.K. by
Anchor Brendon Ltd, Essex

For Alan, Anthony, Anthony, Brian Chester, Colin,
David, Don, Eden, Harold, Hilary, Ion, Michelle, Nigel, Pat,
Paul, Steve, Simon, Terence and all my other publishers
past and present.

ONE

Vernon Hemlock caressed the bulbous base of his brandy balloon with almost as much lascivious pleasure as he devoted to the sublimely erotic bottom of his mistress, Romany Flange. The grey-blue coil of smoke from his enormous Romeo y Julieta eddied towards the deliciously rude ceiling painted for the house's original owner in 1864. Hemlock gazed wistfully at the sportive nymphs, shepherds and satyrs frolicking about a Tuscan countryside in which every piece of topography seemed to be a phallic symbol of one kind or another.

Vernon Hemlock smiled. It had been a good day at the office. The six-monthly sales conference of Big Books PLC, the publishing giant he had created with a ten thousand pound loan from his old chum Barrington-Fingest, was an occasion of ever-increasing self-satisfaction. Big Books grew bigger and bigger. As the books got bigger the cheques got bigger and so did the American sales and the film options and the enormous co-produced TV series. Hemlock published fewer and fewer titles every year, but such titles! Today had seen the announcement of *The Royal Family Cookbook*, a certain bestseller for Christmas with the astonishing innovation of edible pages. Biochemists in Taiwan had come up with a revolutionary form of rice paper which could be impregnated with whatever flavour you wanted. An edible Royal Family! Hemlock purred.

Tonight as so often he decided to take a last look downstairs in the library basement where he kept his magnificent collection of erotica and pornography. He was not certain whether he would be bedding Romany tonight or whether he would have to make do with his wife but whatever was in store it always helped to have a last salivating linger over the goodies in the basement. He rather fancied a look at the Scandinavian section.

He took the lift to the basement, inserted the plastic card which was the only way to get through the computer-controlled security doors and swayed over to the stack marked 'S'. 'S' was for 'Sade', and for 'Sweden' and 'Swiss Army Knife'; for 'Sachertorte' and 'Syphilis' and 'Scrotum' and 'Sarcophagus' and, indeed, for 'Sex' itself. There was more in 'S' even than in 'F'.

The entire collection was willed to the Getty Museum in California. Perhaps it should have gone to the nation, but if the nation had it it would be kept on locked shelves whereas in California it would be available to all. Besides, Hemlock relished the thought of the nation's predicament in having to decide whether or not an export licence would be granted. It might be filth but it was unique filth and priceless, too. There was a Leonardo cartoon of mind-boggling ingenuity; a Picasso of geometric perfection and physical impossibility; a Laughing Cavalier who saw a joke unsuspected by anyone who knew only the original; a Constable in which the beasts of the field were as bestial as Henry VIII in Holbein's extraordinarily irreverent portrayal *The Monarch at Rest in the Dedans*.

Hemlock exhaled and licked his lips, then turned the wheel to prise the shelves apart. He had always had a weakness for this sort of thing ever since his first glimpse of *Health and Efficiency* on Platform 3 at Bristol Temple Meads so many years before. He was one of nature's voyeurs. It was what made him such a successful publisher.

The floor was shiny tiled and his slippered feet made a sibilant lounge lizard sound as they greased along the newly opened aisle. At Stradivarius he paused. There was something extraordinarily titillating about erotic stringed instruments of the seventeen hundreds. He removed the bulky vellum volume and licked his lips again.

He was so engrossed that he never heard the turn of the screw, or noticed that the shelving was starting to move together again. It was only when his brandy glass toppled, spilling VSOP over a naked nun playing the cello, that he realised something was wrong. The shelving was power-assisted so that within seconds he was trapped. For a moment there was a pause, and from what seemed a long way off he heard laughter, muffled by volume upon volume of priceless erotica.

The tip of his cigar caught the edge of the page, which started to smoulder, but his arms were now trapped at his side and he could not move to put out the fire. Coughing now he began to call out but the shelves ground on, tightening their grip remorselessly to the accompaniment of the distant laughter.

The fire triggered the smoke detectors about half an hour later, by which time it had gained a strong enough hold to effectively destroy the entire collection. Luckily it was well insured. Oddly enough it was not until morning that a thoughtful police constable opened up the shelves marked 'S' and discovered Vernon Hemlock of Big Books PLC.

He was, of course, extremely dead.

TWO

Simon Bognor and his wife Monica were guests at Hemlocks that night. Not that Bognor was what you might call 'bookish'. Not in the modern sense. Apart from one or two whodunits and other 'genre' novels he eschewed contemporary fiction, leaving it to his wife Monica, a devotee of the East Anglian school of writing which drove Bognor into terrible rages. Bognor believed that the novel had died at around the outbreak of the Great War.

Occasionally Monica would encourage him to read something safe and old fashioned like the latest Amis but after a few pages Bognor would give up, muttering, and return to Dickens or Mrs Gaskell. He was none too keen on non-fiction, either. 'If it's true it's boring; if it's not boring it's bound to be lies.' He was becoming curmudgeonly in middle-age, only saved from being a tiresome fogey himself by his contempt and distaste for those who really were members of that peculiar brotherhood. 'Teenage pensioners', Bognor called them with all the middle's hatred of extremes.

It was this hostile attitude towards modern literature which had led Parkinson to propose that Bognor should prepare the Board of Trade's preliminary working (mauve) paper on 'The Publishing Industry'.

'This should force you into the twentieth century, laddie,' Parkinson had said, announcing the project. 'I want no leaf unturned. A Good Book is the precious life-blood of a master spirit and nowadays Good Books are Big Bucks. I want none of your mimsy Oxford college nonsense about aesthetic values. This is a commercial business. No claptrap about starving novelists in Bloomsbury attics. No *Times Literary Supplement* arty-fartiness. We need to know about the sort of books people read, Bognor. Not pseudo-intellectual sociology lecturers. Real people.'

4

'I see,' Bognor had said, biting his lip dolefully. 'I see' had been his standard response to Parkinson ever since he had first joined the Board of Trade so many years before.

And there was another project not known to Parkinson. Now that Bognor was in his forties, contemporaries of his seemed to have risen to positions of eminence and even power. One, a porcine economist called Weinstube, was a junior minister in the new Socialist Coalition Government. His curious task was concerned with propaganda and the rewriting of history. After only a few weeks in office Weinstube had come up with a long list of utterly uncommercial titles such as *The People's Friend – The Role of the Job Centre in Post-Industrial Society* and a two-volume life of Patrick Gordon Walker. One such project was a history of the Board of Trade. Meeting Bognor at an Apocrypha College Society Dinner he had, after port, asked Bognor if he would take on the volume dealing with the Special Investigations Department, where, God help him, Bognor had worked all his adult life.

Weinstube might have been a silly man but he wasn't stupid. His silver tongue had secured considerable sums of government money for his department and its publications. He had also negotiated a number of deals with Vernon Hemlock. These were unorthodox and the only certainty about them was that they reflected personal financial credit on the two principals. This was arranged through carefully selected third parties acting through a discreet bank in Liechtenstein and was reckoned by both Weinstube and Hemlock to be foolproof. Thus it was – up to a point and in a manner of speaking – that Bognor became a Big Book author. Not that Hemlock would be publishing under his Big Book imprint. That would be wholly inappropriate. The almost certainly unsalable Weinstube books would be published by Aspen and Larch, the small subsidiary house Hemlock had acquired for just such contingencies. Aspen and Larch dealt in rubbish of various kinds and operated mainly as a tax loss. The publishing industry was full of Aspens and Larches.

'I suppose they'll have to call off the sales conference,' said Bognor, peering morosely out to sea. He and Monica were taking a modest constitutional along the front after breakfast. It

5

was noticeable that Hemlock's demise had had very little effect on their appetites. Nor on anyone else's.

'I doubt it.' Monica yawned. 'Whatever time did those perfectly bloody fire alarms go off?'

'About half an hour after I nodded off,' said Bognor. 'Worst possible time. Just when you're into deep sleep. It could be quite dangerous.' Bognor had been reading an article about sleep patterns in the 'specialists' page in the *Daily Telegraph* – the page which was always illustrated with pictures of building blocks and arrows. It looked like the instruction manual for a build-it-yourself Finnish picnic table which still lay half-constructed in the Bognors' garden shed back home.

'You were snoring. I was still asleep.'

'Lucky you!' Bognor spoke feelingly. 'That means you've had more rest than I've had. I've actually had a minus quantity of sleep, being woken up like that.' He flexed his paunch and turned inland, breathing deeply. 'I must say I do like the seaside,' he said.

'You can't like Byfleet-next-the-Sea.' Monica spoke with the asperity of an insulted and quite exhausted wife but her husband seemed not to notice.

'Oh, but I do,' he said, 'I think it's enchanting.' He gazed along the promenade, absorbing the shuttered soft-drink stalls, the bolted bathing huts, the upturned dinghies, the tarpaulin over the stacked deckchairs which flapped in the winter wind. 'Where else in the world would you get this sense of desolation? "Listen! you hear the grating roar of pebbles which the waves . . . er . . . te-tum . . . and fling . . . until . . . "'

'"Draw back, and fling at their return, up the high strand", you illiterate oaf!' Monica snorted her exasperation. 'Come on!' she said, 'we'd better get back to Hemlocks and see what's going on.' She started to stride back, taking long sensible strides in her flat, sensible shoes.

Bognor had to run to catch up, then fell into step. 'Then there's something about "eternal sadness", isn't there?'

'"Begin, and cease, and then again begin,
With tremulous cadence slow, and bring
The eternal note of sadness in."'

6

'That's right.' He spoke with approval and also the bogus knowledgeable manner of someone who knows he is a bit of a ninny but does not need or wish to be reminded of it. 'Poor old Hemlock!' he said, after a pause. 'The eternal note of sadness certainly sounded for him.'

'He was a rapacious slug,' said Monica, 'a nasty, greedy, mercenary brute.'

'Steady on!' said Bognor. 'He was my publisher.'

'You hadn't signed anything.'

'No, but we had an understanding.'

'Understanding be jiggered.'

'I don't think you're being entirely fair, Monica. And anyway he's dead now.'

'Good riddance!' Mrs Bognor lengthened her stride, leaving her husband bobbing in her wake.

Bognor leant against an Edwardian street-lamp lovingly preserved by the Byfleet and District Townswomen's Guild and panted. A tattered poster advertising August's end-of-the-pier show leered down at him from the pebbledashed wall of a gentleman's lavatory and a couple of seagulls mewed overhead. They could have been fighting or mating, he wasn't sure, being no ornithologist. Came to the same thing in the end. In the distance he watched his wife buffeting against the wind, closing in on the grey sub-Lutyens bulk of Hemlocks. It had been built for Norbiton, the margarine magnate, who had perished in a flying-boat accident off Salerno before he could take up residence. A cross between the Cenotaph and Anne Hathaway's cottage – a gross pillbox, half-timbered and bloated, barnacled with turrets and conservatories and roof gardens. Hemlock had bought it from nuns in the sixties for a song.

Bognor sighed. Monica was little more than a matchstick person now. Maddening woman, though he was fond of the old bag in his way. And she of him, he thought, ruefully. He sighed again and began to rumble after her, flatfooted, hung-over and a little depressed. He wondered if he would see the year out or would end up dead like Hemlock, lightly toasted between two library shelves. A wave broke close by, sending a shower of spray over his rising forehead. He turned up the collar of his coat and paced purposefully back towards the great house. He was afraid his troubles were only just beginning.

'They're all in the library,' said Hastings. Hastings was the butler. He had been with Hemlock since the beginning – first as office, errand and tea boy, later as a rep. He claimed never to have read a book in his life and nothing about him suggested this to be untrue. He had sussed Bognor as a Right Wally the moment he saw him. Most of the other guests got a 'sir' or 'madam' from Hastings, mainly in the hope of a tip when they left. Not Bognor.

'Right,' said Bognor, with an air of purpose. He handed over his Burberry and straightened his tie.

'Am I to join them?' he asked.

'The Chief Inspector said he gave instructions for no one to leave the house.' Hastings accepted the coat with ill grace. 'And that included you. If I were you I'd cut along sharpish and say sorry like a good boy.'

Bognor said nothing, just pulled at his cuff and gave Hastings one of his famous but unconvincing withering looks.

'Git!' mouthed Hastings in a stage whisper.

Bognor ignored him. He had long since learned never to bandy words with a butler.

The library door was stiff and squeaky so that he entered the room with a fanfare of protesting hinge. The room was uncarpeted so that even if he went on tiptoe, which he did, every step was noisy. He hated making this sort of entrance. It always reminded him of that terrible morning so many years before when he had arrived late for morning chapel and walked down the aisle under the sniggering gaze of five hundred boys. The headmaster, gowned and mortar-boarded on his wooden throne, had looked on with no amusement at all. Beatable offence.

Now that he was a grown-up, indeed middle-aged, person, Bognor knew that he should not be embarrassed at being the centre of attention. He certainly shouldn't be fazed by the censure of some two-bit Detective Chief Inspector and a roomful of Vernon Hemlock's bestselling-author houseguests.

But he was.

'You must be Bognor.' The Chief Inspector was the sort of pedestrian oaf Bognor abominated. He wore the suit one associated with professional footballers and his hair was cut short with the suspicion of a Derek Hatton bob at the back. His was the sharp, fashionable, scented appearance which Bognor mistrusted very much indeed. He used to think he disliked the old-fashioned detectives in trench coats and chunky black shoes, but he preferred them to the new breed.

'Simon Bognor, Board of Trade,' he said, trying to sound polite.

'I gave instructions that no one was to leave the house.' The DCI dabbed at his ducky little moustache.

'I'm sorry. The instructions didn't reach me.'

Bognor sat down heavily on a set of library steps next to Arthur Green, author of *The Billion Lire Breakfast*, *The Million Dollar Martini*, *The Lunch that ended the World* and *Last Supper*. Mr Green, mousey as ever, gave him an encouraging glance and a quarter-smile. Like so many authors he was as near the opposite of his hero, Lance Remington, as it was possible to imagine.

'Honey, I had no instructions!' This was Marlene Glopff, the sinuous raven-haired superstar of the American soap *Homer*. The series was not, as Bognor had supposed, a Greek epic but something to do with baseball. Miss Glopff was a fitness freak who lifted weights and lived almost exclusively on wheatgerm and carrot-juice. She had just produced ('written' was not the word) her first book, *Working Out with Glopff*.

'I gave instructions that no one was to leave the house, Miss Glopff,' said the Chief Inspector. 'Those instructions were perfectly explicit and I expect them to be carried out. I don't wish to have to charge anyone with obstructing the course of justice.'

Marlene Glopff pouted but said nothing.

Milton Capstick, characteristically, took exception to the policeman's words. Capstick had 'authored' (a favourite Hemlock word) a hugely successful series of self-help and improvement volumes. As the onlie begetter of *The True Self*, *Looking After Number One* and *The First Billion*, Capstick believed in permanent self-advertisement. He was never put down.

'There's clearly been a breakdown in communications, Officer,' he said. As he spoke, his bow tie bobbed up and down in time to his Adam's apple. His blazer was very clean and his grey flannels beautifully creased. He was almost suave, but, like most of Hemlock's authors, there was – to Bognor's practised and jaundiced, if bleary, eye – a built-in phoniness. People who wrote Big Books were almost always unreal.

This certainly applied to Danvers Warrington who spoke next. 'Dashed if I knew anything about being confined to barracks, old fruit,' he said, waving the stem of an ornate curlicued meerschaum at the Chief Inspector. 'I'd have been out for the old crack of dawn constitutional if it wasn't for a twinge of the old malaria. Never leaves you, malaria. Like sandfly fever. Once bitten, twice . . . well, I certainly never heard anything about being put in jankers.' Warrington was Hemlock's famous wine writer: *Warrington on Wine*, *More Wine with Warrington*, *Another Glass with Warrington*, *Pass the Plonk with Warrington*. On the television show that he hosted for Wessex TV he invariably appeared in loud-check plus-fours with knee-length canary stockings. Also a monocle. He was in just such an outfit now.

'That will do, thank you,' said the DCI. He put his hand in his jacket pocket like Prince Philip and surveyed the little group in silence, moving his head from left to right, pausing for meaningful eyeball-to-eyeball contact with each person in turn. Bognor guessed the idea was to get everyone to look away before he did. It must have been something from the latest Scotland Yard manual on how to interrogate terrorists. Bognor was not going to become involved in eyeball wrestling at this stage of the proceedings so he stared resolutely at Hemlock's *Encyclopaedia Britannica* which was handily situated a few yards behind Inspector Bumstead's left elbow.

'We believe', said the Inspector when he had finished this lingering tour d'horizon, 'that we are dealing with a murder.'

No one spoke until Monica Bognor, a woman given to speaking her mind and much less susceptible to intimidation than her husband or indeed anybody else present.

'Are you implying that one of us killed Vernon Hemlock?' she asked.

'That's not what I said.'

'I didn't say you did. I merely wanted to know if that's what you were implying. There's a difference.'

'I have reason to believe that the deceased did not die due to natural causes.'

'Goodness, how exciting!' It was Cynthia Midgely, the distaff side of the Midgely writing team which performed under the joint by-line of Miranda Howard. She and her husband Wilfred used to work on the same local paper until hitting on a royal book formula which had made them both millionaires. Theirs was the newly announced *Royal Family Cookbook*. Its predecessors included *The Royal Family Bedside Book, Royal Party Games, The Queen Mum, Good Queen Bess, Charlie's Aunt, More Royal Party Games* and *The Royal Family Bedside Book 1979* – and an annual sequel in each of the following years. Cynthia was easily excited – an attribute which contributed to the notorious but commercially successful purple gush of the books. Wilfred supplied the research, though neither of them had ever actually seen a member of the Royal Family in the flesh. When confronted with this, both Cynthia and Wilfred used to reply archly that Lady Antonia Fraser had never met Mary Queen of Scots and look at her. This always went down very well on the Wogan show.

This time Cynthia had not meant to speak so loudly. She coloured and said in a coy simper, 'I mean, how perfectly dreadful!'

'Perfectly dreadful indeed,' said Bumstead. 'There are no signs of a forcible entry having been effected into the house and I am therefore driven to the conclusion that whoever killed Mr Hemlock was staying in the house. Not to put too fine a point on it this was an inside job.'

Looking round, Bognor saw that the company was, if not struck dumb, at least extremely subdued by this news. The most affected were, predictably enough, the two women known to be in Hemlock's life: his wife Audrey, the foreign rights director, and his mistress Romany Flange, brightest of the Big Books editors whose eye for the main chance was unerring. Miss Flange was supposed to be enamoured of Merlin Glatt who was on the verge of becoming an absolutely enormous poet. Hemlock had not allowed him over the threshold – not just because of his place in the affections of Romany Flange but also because he had signed a contract for an erotic bestiary with Andover Strobe, Hemlock's biggest rival in the world of books.

The Inspector smiled a thin, professional smile designed to freeze bone marrow.

'Everybody who slept in the house is in this room now,' he said. He stared at Bognor.

'You're forgetting the staff,' said Bognor. 'This may have been an inside job but there's no reason why it shouldn't have been a downstairs one. Consider the butler.'

'Bugger the butler,' said the Inspector. Bognor seemed to be getting on the policeman's nerves. This was exactly where he wanted to be.

'I'm sorry.' Bognor felt a sudden access of confidence. Reaching into his inside pocket he found his impressive laminated ID and waved it at the policeman. 'I do have a certain professional standing in cases like this,' he said, 'and my view is that you would be unwise to bugger the butler, whatever your inclination. As a member of the Special Investigations Department of the Board of Trade I do have some experience of crime, and . . .' he paused here for dramatic effect '. . . murder.'

The DCI now looked quite angry. 'Is that so?'

'That is so,' said Bognor, confidence flowing into him along with the irritation.

'I do hope, Mr Bognor, that you are not going to be a nuisance.'

Bognor spread his hands to indicate that he personally had no intention of doing anything at all which might in any way interfere with whatever it was the DCI was up to. He also managed to convey, with surprising skill, that in his opinion the Detective Inspector might be making a big mistake.

At this point Monica decided to intervene. Hostile she might be in private, but in public she could be loyal as a lion. She did not like to see her husband patronised or bullied. Still less did she like to see him make a fool of himself.

'Chief Inspector,' she said, smiling, 'I wonder if I might have a word with you in private?'

'I shall be having words with everyone in private,' said the Inspector, 'and in the meantime I must ask all of you to go to your rooms and under no circumstances to discuss anything at all with each other – least of all the deceased and the manner of his demise.'

He paused again. 'One of these officers will call you when I need you.' He nodded curtly at the impossibly young constables who stood at either side of the library door. 'Now if you'd all make your way upstairs in silence I'd just like Dr Belgrave to stay behind, please.'

Dr Belgrave was an iron-grey spinster in a maroon trilby. She wore gloves, smoked a cigarette through a holder, sported steel rimmed specs and was the author of *The British Approach to Sex, Sex and the United States, La Vie Sexuelle – an Analysis of the French Way of Love* and *Behind the Net Curtain – a Study in Suburban Sin*. In Bognor's view she was almost certainly a man, bearing, as she did, a remarkable resemblance to one of the greatest of all Welsh scrum-halves. She was alleged to have been Hemlock's adviser concerning the erotic dungeon below-stairs where he had met his end. As far as sex was concerned, her interest was said to be entirely theoretical and intellectual – though even there Bognor had his doubts.

Monica was not so easily fobbed off.

'Ann,' she said, grasping Dr Belgrave by the elbow and propelling her towards the door as everyone began to leave, 'I won't be more than a second. But I do feel someone has to save this silly little man from himself.'

THREE

Five minutes later Bognor stood at the bedroom window watching the waves lash the sea wall. Pondering the arbitrary way in which the grim reaper gathered in the harvest, he was roused from his reverie by his wife bursting in with as much ferocity as the sea outside.

'What a perfectly bloody little man!' she said, chest heaving. She was a formidable sight when roused and she was plainly roused now. 'He more or less told me to mind my own business.'

Bognor gazed out at the troubled waters and wished he was on the other side, abroad, away from tiresome, unexpected murders which threatened to upset the equilibrium of his ways.

'He as good as told me that we were suspects ourselves.'

'I suppose, in the circumstances, that's not unreasonable.'

'Don't be ridiculous. What can you mean?'

'If Hemlock was murdered last night then presumably he was murdered by someone who was staying in the house overnight. That includes us.'

'No intelligent investigator could seriously include us among a list of murder suspects. It's preposterous.'

'He's not an intelligent investigator, he's a spivvy little half-wit.'

Monica sat down on the bed. 'I'd no idea you'd taken against him quite so strongly. His name's Bumstead, by the way, Arthur Bumstead.'

'There's a footballer called Bumstead,' said Bognor. 'Plays for Chelsea.'

'So?'

'So nothing. But it's not a fortunate name. He'd have done a sight better if he'd changed it. There's a lot in a name.'

'It doesn't seem to have done the Chief Inspector much harm.'

14

'He's done well in spite of it.' A gust of wind caught an abandoned deckchair and tossed it against the railings where it stuck flapping. It reminded Bognor of a dying bird, a dying bird in the garish stripes of some impossibly minor public school or designed by a state-of-the-art advertising agency. It was the sort of thing Vernon Hemlock would have enjoyed as a publicity stunt – spraying a whole lot of birds in fluorescent paint and releasing them at his sales conference. He would have worked in some naked ladies as well, being such a one for naked ladies. Real and imaginary. If it hadn't been for his obsession with naked ladies he might still be alive and well and . . .

'Simon! You're not listening.'

He shook his head. He had noticed that his attention span had been diminishing recently, his boredom threshold getting lower.

'I'm sorry,' he said, 'I was thinking.'

'We're going to need to do a lot of that.'

'Yes.' Bognor was not looking forward to the prospect. He wished people wouldn't get themselves killed while he was visiting. It had happened before.

The telephone rang. Both Bognors knew instinctively who it was. Only one person they could think of knew where they were. Only one person invariably got in touch after a corpse had appeared in Bognor's life. He was Bognor's vulture, an office undertaker. Where Bognor was so often and so unwittingly the harbinger of death, Parkinson was its confirmation.

Monica picked up the receiver and handed it to her spouse with a 'Guess who?' expression and a ritual 'I think it's for you-hoo!'

'Bognor,' said Bognor.

'Done it again, eh, Bognor?' Parkinson sounded almost pleased, as if glad to have his suspicions confirmed even though they were rather terrible. Like a weather forecaster walking into a blizzard of his own predicting.

'You've heard, then?'

'One gets to hear things before they happen in this job, as you should know by now, Bognor. I'm told your friend Mr Hemlock was squashed to death between two sliding shelves in his library.'

'That's about the size of it.'

'Rather less than the size he used to be,' said Parkinson without mirth. 'I take it you're assisting the police with their enquiries.'

'No chance. The DCI seems to take a dim view of me at the moment. It's mutual.'

'That won't do, Bognor. Won't do at all. You know the rules. Maximum co-operation with the law at all times. At least on the face of it. You must put yourself entirely at the Chief Inspector's disposal while reporting back to me at all times.'

'I've tried,' said Bognor. 'He doesn't want me at his disposal.'

There was a long pause. Bognor sensed irritation pulsing down the line like an electric charge. He could picture the Parkinson brow, sweaty, empurpled. The old man was more crotchety than ever as retirement loomed, especially as the coveted 'K' still eluded him.

'You must try harder,' he said eventually. 'Meanwhile I'll have a word with the Chief Constable, though frankly he's a bit of a bugger himself. Downright obstructive in the drugged banana boat business in 'eighty-two. Some of these people don't seem to understand the jurisdiction of SIDBOT. Think they're God Almighty and can do as they please. I may have to go over some heads and apply for a Q4 but meanwhile you butter your man up. And call me back this afternoon. I want this cleared up sharpish and with no embarrassment to the Department or the Board.'

'Righty-ho!' Bognor did not feel as jaunty as he tried to sound.

Monica had broken a nail. Worrying at it with an emery board she said, 'How long can he keep us here?'

'He can't,' said Bognor. 'At least not in theory. We're perfectly free to come and go as we please. But in practice I'd say we're stuck here till about lunch. Then I should guess one or other of our little company is going to plead an urgent business appointment and cut and run.'

'Guess who'll be first?'

'Milton Capstick,' said Bognor. 'His self-esteem demands it.'

'I was going to say Capstick. He's awful.'

'They're all awful,' Bognor sighed. 'Only some are more awful than others. I think I'm getting a cold. I shouldn't have gone for that walk. Ruined my relationship with the gentleman of the police and my constitution all in one go.' He blew his nose into a blue-and-white spotted handkerchief. It was rather grubby.

'Who do *you* think did it?' Monica sounded as if her own mind was made up already.

'They're all unpleasant enough. And everyone had the opportunity.'

'I thought you needed a special card to get into the basement?'

'Who told you that?'

'Audrey Hemlock. We had a tête-à-tête in the loo yesterday. She was having a bit of a weep.'

'You never told me.'

'You never asked. Anyway, it didn't seem particularly interesting at the time.'

'What was she blubbing about?'

'What do you think? Her bloody husband. Whenever you see women crying their eyes out in the loo it's because of some ghastly man.'

Bognor frowned. 'What in particular?'

'Honestly, Simon, you can be an awful oaf sometimes. No one enjoys constant public humiliation.'

'You mean Romany Flange?'

'Yes. Everyone knew she was Hemlock's mistress. Everyone knew about the dirty books in the basement. Audrey thought we were all sniggering. Or pitying her. She couldn't make up her mind which was worse.'

'Poor old Audrey. Gives her a motive, though.' Bognor chewed his lip and wondered if he might smoke a cheroot. He decided against. They made him wheeze and Monica would complain that they made the sheets smell.

'I don't think you'll find any shortage of motive,' said Monica, 'but Audrey certainly didn't have one of those open-sesame plastic cards for the basement.'

17

'Did anyone except Hemlock?'

'That ridiculous butler, I think. And there would have been a spare somewhere.'

'On the other hand,' said Bognor, 'it's perfectly possible Hemlock didn't shut the door behind him. He was several sheets in the wind when I last saw him.'

'How long after I came up were you?' Monica had retired at ten-thirty, announcing that she was going to read another chapter of Margaret Atwood. Atwood, though a biggish author, especially for a Canadian, was not on the Big Books list. Hemlock had not been amused.

'Pseudo-intellectual garbage,' he had slurred, laying a fleshy hand on Monica's bottom as she walked past.

Bognor frowned. 'About an hour,' he said. 'Hemlock was banging on about export sales markets and telling smutty stories. People were drifting away one by one until it was just me, Warrington and Capstick. When I came in you were snoring with the Atwood wide open beside you.'

'So when you left it was just the three men.'

'Yes.' Bognor thought as hard as possible. 'They were all having what Hemlock – inevitably – referred to as one for the road.'

'Maybe Hemlock invited them down to the basement for a little leer?'

'It's possible,' said Bognor; 'there was no sight or sound of anyone when I was looking for the milk. I assumed they'd gone up to bed. Maybe they'd gone downstairs instead.'

'You what?' Monica seemed astonished.

'Assumed they'd gone up to bed.'

'No. Before that. You said you'd gone looking for milk.'

Bognor blushed. 'I had a sudden craving. Besides, I thought in view of the alcohol intake it might be a good idea. A lining for the stomach.'

'Idiot,' said Monica. 'That's before you start on the booze, not after. It's supposed to act as a sort of barrier between the wall of the stomach and the alcohol. Pure fantasy.'

'Oh.'

'Anyway, you're telling me that after you'd come up here you

18

suddenly decided it would be a good wheeze to nip out again and go in search of milk.'

'I told you. I had a craving. I couldn't sleep because of all the noise you were making, so it seemed only sensible to get some peace and quiet and some milk into the bargain.'

'So you were on the toot at the very moment Vernon Hemlock was snuffing it?'

Bognor grimaced. 'I was not on the toot. I merely wanted a drink of milk.'

'But you see what I'm getting at?'

'No.' Bognor was becoming decidedly tetchy.

Monica sighed. 'If', she said, 'you were larking about the house in the middle of the night, then you might perfectly well have roamed in the direction of the Hemlock erotic library, twiddled a few knobs and sent poor Vernon off into eternity.'

'Don't be silly.'

'I'm not being silly.'

'But you know I didn't.'

'I know you didn't because I'm married to you. Chief Inspector Bumstead isn't.'

Bognor scratched the back of his head. There was some truth in what Monica said. In retrospect it had been foolish to go looking for milk. Like so much in life it had seemed a good idea at the time – like joining the Board of Trade fresh from Oxford, marrying Monica, supporting Somerset at cricket. Grief had often had a disagreeable habit of treading on the heels of pleasure as far as Bognor was concerned. Not a very dramatic form of grief but what your average modern doctor would describe as 'discomfort'. Like toothache or an ulcer. Something you were supposed to suffer in silence.

'You're not seriously suggesting that Bumstead is going to suspect me of being the murderer?'

'It's perfectly possible. He more or less said we were all under suspicion. Once he finds you have no alibi I should think he's bound to think you did it. Worse than no alibi. You were actually prowling around.'

'I was not prowling around. I was looking for milk.'

'Yes, darling.'

19

Bognor glowered. Not for the first time he had a sinking feeling that his wife might be right.

'Look at it another way,' he said, a shade desperately; 'if I didn't do it, who did?'

'Haven't the foggiest,' said Monica, 'but in everyone's interests I think we should do our level best to find out. Whatever the DCI thinks.'

'You mean start questioning people on our own?'

'On *your* own. You have the authority: impressive ID, plausible manner. And Parkinson will have that Q4 before long.'

'He may not get a Q4. And that little tick was very specific about not discussing Hemlock.'

'Don't be so wet. Let's start with Warrington. He's the most obvious poseur.'

Bognor was not enthusiastic but he was beginning to see that in the absence of a bona fide culprit he might well find himself in serious trouble.

He picked up the phone. 'Mr Warrington, please,' he said, sensing the butler's contempt which communicated itself down the telephone as magically as Parkinson's annoyance.

After a pause a voice said 'Warrington'. The voice was the product of two decades of wine tastings in city livery halls and cellars. At least that was what it was obviously intended to convey. Unmistakable. And extremely bankable.

Bognor had no trouble persuading Warrington that they should meet. Bognor had guessed from television that, apart from a drop of 'an interesting little Cru Bourgeois I picked up on my way back from a weekend with Sidney Rothschild', there was nothing Warrington liked more than the sound of his own voice. Especially when listened to with deference. Bognor had managed to imply that his deference would be extreme, that he would be the perfect audience. Bognor had not implied in any way that he regarded Warrington as a suspect. Had he done so Warrington would not have played ball. Instead he had told the nation's greatest wine bore that he wanted to pick his brain and ask his opinions since he was bound to have one or two that Bognor might like to be entitled to. Reflecting on this, Danvers

20

Warrington polished his monocle with a red-and-white spotted handkerchief rusty with snuff stains and positively purred.

They met in Warrington's room. Warrington had evidently conceived a dislike for 'our friend from the constabulary', but he wasn't prepared to run the risk of being caught in the corridors. 'Mister Wine in cells for contempt' was not something he relished. Like many very conceited men he was also a fearful coward.

'Aha!' he said, opening the door and peering theatrically in both directions before bundling them in with much fluster, 'Aha!'

Mr and Mrs Bognor sat down on the bed which, they both noticed, had been very well and freshly made, unlike their own which had not been touched. Warrington sat in a hall porter's chair in blue leather. He crossed his legs and pulled at one of the canary yellow stockings.

'Before we begin,' he said, 'I wonder if I might see some formal identification? I don't like to seem unduly fussy but in the circumstances I think you'll agree one can't be too careful.'

Bognor handed him his shiny laminated Board of Trade card with the new regulation colour photograph which made him look less like a man with a price on his head than the old black and white one. It showed a pudgy face of an alarming, luminous red. Warrington looked at it through his monocle.

'Mrs Bognor is not, I take it, with the Board?' he said.

'I'm just with Simon,' said Monica.

'Quite.' Danvers Warrington pursed his lips in the familiar, pained expression which always preceded one of his famous profundities.

'The dog barks but the caravan moves on,' he said.

It was Bognor's turn to say 'Quite'.

'We writers', he continued, 'are what you might call a rum kettle of fish. Not a lot of love lost, if you see what I mean.'

Bognor nodded.

'I expect I mentioned that I get a twinge of the old sandfly fever now and again?'

The Bognors nodded again.

'You'd think, wouldn't you, that in a houseful of guests, and

21

colleagues at that, that someone would venture a word of sympathy. But no, not a dickie bird. It's perfectly plain that every last one of my fellow scribes thinks it's just another of Danvers' dashed affectations. It leaves a man very low, I can tell you, especially when it strikes in the still small watches. Picked it up in the Malayan show. Suppose you were too young for that.' He jabbed his meerschaum in the general direction of the bed.

'I missed national service,' said Bognor.

'Pity,' said Warrington. 'Makes a man of you. Where was I?'

'You were saying there was no love lost between writers.'

'You're not a writer chappie?'

'Not really.' Bognor did not feel obliged to expound on his projected history of the Special Investigations Department.

'Difficult to understand for someone who's not been touched by the muse.' He gazed at the bowl of his meerschaum as if embarrassed at being touched by the muse. He reminded Bognor of a born-again Christian bearing witness at Wembley or on the TV God-slot.

'The grape and the muse,' he went on; 'it's a rare privilege to have been visited by both.'

'Are you saying that this particular collection of writers did not get on with each other?' Monica, as always, was keen to get to the point. Warrington was irritated at having his stately digressions interrupted.

'As you will certainly have noticed, Mrs Bognor, very few of our company could be described as writers in the true meaning of the word. Self-help manuals and royal scrapbooks are scarcely what one might describe as "literature" in the sense that a gentleman would use the term.'

'I understood some of Dr Belgrave's stuff was considered rather . . . I mean, didn't Germaine Greer do a piece in the *Literary* . . . ?'

'Oh, pish tush, Bognor, pish tush. Let us not beat about the bush. You and I are *hommes du monde*. You know as well as I that Miss Belgrave's emanations are pornography simple if not pure.' He gave a short laugh. This slid into a pipe-smoker's hack which he had some difficulty in curtailing.

When he had stopped coughing he said, 'The fact is that practically every person in this house hates the guts of practically every other person. But I'll tell you something else: almost the only thing which stopped us hating each other was Hemlock. We may have hated each other but we loathed him.'

'Ah,' said Bognor. 'No shortage of motive, then. Why was that?'

Warrington laughed again. 'I can see you really aren't an *auteur*,' he said. 'No man is a hero to his valet, least of all his publisher.'

Bognor did not question this curious sentence. The sentiment behind it was clear enough.

'Would you believe, Mr Bognor,' Warrington lowered his voice, 'that the standard Big Book contract stipulates a five per cent royalty, rising only to ten? *Pass the Plonk with Warrington* was the first British wine book to sell in Japan. Its American advance was a million dollars. It took me months to get a single penny out of them. And then it was only because Audrey Hemlock's a decent woman *au fond*.'

'So you weren't crazy about Hemlock?'

'I should bloody well think not.'

'What exactly happened after I went up to bed last night?'

'I didn't kill him if that's what you mean.'

'It's not, actually, but as far as I can see you and Capstick were the last people to see him alive. Did you all go to bed at the same time?'

'No.'

Was it Bognor's imagination or did Warrington's negative come a shade too sharp?

'We finished our drinks, then Hemlock gave Capstick a dig in the ribs, a literal dig in the ribs, and asked if he'd like one last one downstairs.'

'He didn't ask you?'

'Not exactly. I mean he didn't positively not ask me but he didn't make me feel wanted either. If he did ask the question he phrased it so that I was obviously expected to say no. Anyway, I wanted bed. I was worn out. Bored, too.'

'Why stay so long?'

'Part of the function of a sales conference', said Warrington wearily, 'is to ingratiate yourself with the boss. Big Books sales conferences are just an opportunity for Hemlock to arouse a wholesale display of absolutely sickening sycophancy.'

'Did you know about "downstairs"?'

'Everyone knows about "downstairs". It's been in *Private Eye* every fortnight for the last ten years.'

'But you'd never seen it for yourself?'

'Not my cup of tea. I prefer my pleasures to be in the flesh, if you'll pardon the expression. I've never seen the attraction of voyeurism.'

'Not', said Bognor, 'that Mr Hemlock was averse to a bit of real-life nooky?'

'It's amazing what power and money can do. Romany Flange, Marlene Glopff. They wouldn't have looked twice at that odious little toad if he hadn't been loaded with cash and influence.'

'I knew about Romany Flange,' said Bognor, 'but not Glopff.'

'*Working Out with Glopff*,' said Warrington. 'He always liked an element of *double entendre*. It's Audrey I feel sorry for.'

There was a silence while Warrington fed tobacco into his pipe. The tobacco was in a pouch that looked like moleskin. It smelt of cellar.

'So the last you saw of Hemlock was him and Capstick heading towards the basement?'

'Yes.'

'Then what?'

'I went to bed, slept soundly and woke to find all this *brouhaha*.'

'And that's it?'

'That's it.' A cloud of smoke wafted towards the ceiling. It smelt of more than three nuns. Warrington recrossed his legs, flaunting canary calves.

'Odds on Capstick,' he said. 'Three to one the butler. Bar the field.'

'What makes you say that?'

'Opportunity,' said Warrington. 'We all had motive because one way or another we were all being ripped off.'

'It's quite rare for an author to murder his publisher,' said Bognor. 'In fact I've never heard of it before.'

'Lack of real opportunity,' said Warrington. 'The motivation is nearly always there but if you think about it your average publisher seldom allows himself to be exposed to the author in what our transatlantic cousins call a "one-on-one situation". I don't mean editors. I mean your average "*grand fromage*". The nearest they ever get to an *à deux* situation with a writer is lunch at the Savoy Grill when one of us has the temerity to complain about the latest ghastly book jacket the art department have stuck on. Or when one of their rivals tries to poach us. The last time I had lunch on my own with Hemlock was at the Savoy Grill after he'd seen me lunching with Andover Strobe at the Neal Street Restaurant.'

'Strobe was trying to poach you?'

'Going through the motions. He knows that it's almost impossible to escape from a Hemlock contract. Houdini himself couldn't have got out of one. Hemlock has option clauses so binding Baden Powell himself couldn't untie them. But Strobe still likes to lunch Big Book authors. It irritates Hemlock. Besides, he has to have names to put on his expense forms.'

'I see.' Bognor was beginning to develop a new understanding of the world of books. 'Why Capstick in particular?' he asked.

'As I said, *mon vieux*, we all had motives.' Warrington waved the pipe in a semi-circle. It trailed smoke like an ancient anarchist's bomb about to explode. 'In his case I suspect it was something to do with the film rights to *Looking After Number One*. The story I heard was that Hemlock wanted Marlene Glopff to star and Arthur Green to do the script. I could be wrong. But if it wasn't that it would be something else. I wouldn't concern yourself unduly with motive. As I said, we've all got plenty of those.'

'Shhh!' Monica's hearing was uncannily keen. At railway stations she was always the first one to pick up the vibrations from the approaching train. Now she had obviously detected an ominous

25

hum from the corridor carpet. 'Someone coming,' she said.

They froze.

She was right. The footsteps were brisk, purposeful and almost certainly official.

'Shouldn't you make a dash for it?' Warrington was agitated.

'Too late,' said Bognor.

'No reason to,' said Monica. 'We have a perfect right to be here. Duty even. You invited us, Mr Warrington.'

'I'd rather you didn't say that, Mrs Bognor. I don't want to run foul of the law. They can be very troublesome, *les flics*. I had a little difficulty with them over a breathalyser business. For sheer malice they were beyond belief. Not overly scrupulous when it came to the truth, either. And because of who I am they seemed to find the whole thing screamingly funny. The ribaldry! You wouldn't believe it.'

They had all hoped that the footsteps were not coming their way but, just as they thought they had passed and were heading away into the distance, they stopped and there was a knock on the door. The knock had the same perfunctory, official sound as the footsteps.

'*Entrez!*' said Warrington, an assumed breeziness fooling neither Mr nor Mrs Bognor.

The door opened and a very young, spotty man with lightly spiked blond hair and a sharp but cheap off-the-peg suit, stood there. He seemed nervous but also hostile.

'Mr Warrington?' he asked.

'Yes,' said Warrington, saying the word slowly through both nostrils just as he did in his famous TV blind tastings.

'Chief Inspector would like a word if you please, sir.'

The 'sir' was not altogether satisfactory. Not enunciated with the proper degree of obeisance.

'Naturally, Officer,' said Warrington, pique overcoming nerves. The word 'Officer' was spoken with the same sort of subtext that had characterised the earlier 'sir'. Bognor made a mental note of 'fifteen all'.

'Before you go, sir,' (thirty-fifteen observed Bognor) 'I wonder if you'd be so kind as to explain what Mr and Mrs Bognor are doing here.'

Warrington was plainly not up to this. He had the conventional lay terror of authority, especially of the police.

'Perfectly all right, Officer,' Bognor decided that this was an opportunity to pull rank, 'I was just asking Mr Warrington one or two questions, in my official capacity.' He flashed his ID in the direction of the young policeman who seemed lamentably unimpressed.

'I'm sorry, sir,' he said, 'but the Chief Inspector's instructions were quite specific. I must ask you to return to your room immediately. You'll understand that I shall have to make a report to the Chief Inspector seeing as how he was so specific about going to your rooms and under no circumstances discussing the matter with anyone else in the house.'

'You have your job to do,' said Bognor, sorely tempted to slip in a quick 'sonny' to push the score on to forty-thirty. He resisted, not wishing to seem petty. He hoped Parkinson had managed to get the Q4, otherwise he might be in trouble. Normally he worked perfectly well with the investigating officers in cases like this. There had been problems, of course. Bognor's highly intuitive and unorthodox approach to crime was not always appreciated by a police force which was bcoming increasingly scientific and logical in its approach. Bognor's view was that the two styles could work together quite satisfactorily with a little give and take. There were moments when all the forensic logic in the world could not conjure up the right solution. He acknowledged that an element of plod and science was sometimes necessary. So why couldn't that sort of investigator recognise that 'flair' and the ability to leap boldly across the hurdles erected in the name of plausibility were also valuable. He supposed that a certain sort of person was always chippy when confronted with real class. Bumstead was obviously just such a person. Classic second-rater.

The expected reaction materialised almost at once. They had scarcely returned to their room when more footsteps sounded, more official, more menacing, more bumptious than before. The knock at the door was barely even a formality.

'What the bloody hell do you think you're playing at, Bognor?' Bumstead was cross. The vein at his temple was throbbing like the cha-cha and there were gobbets of perspiration shining on the dinky little moustache.

'Problem, Inspector?' asked Bognor, pleasantly enough. It took two to have a major row and he had decided not to give the little man that satisfaction.

Bumstead advanced very close so that his head was only a foot or so from Bognor's. They would have been eyeball to eyeball but for the fact – very satisfying to Bognor – that the policeman was a clear six inches shorter. Bognor had only seen this sort of stance adopted by baseball team managers who came on the field of play to complain to officials. They were usually chewing tobacco rather like the stuff Warrington smoked. Bumstead was not chewing tobacco but Bognor noticed with satisfaction that he had some alien object stuck between his two front teeth. A reminder of breakfast, he presumed. Probably a bit of muesli. The DCI looked like a muesli man.

'You're not half as funny as you seem to think, my friend,' said Bumstead. His breath was surprisingly rancid under an overlay of minty toothpaste.

'I don't think I'm in the least bit funny,' said Bognor, equably. 'My wife will tell you that one of my faults is taking myself a great deal too seriously. And as for being your friend, I think not.'

'I could do you, Bognor.'

'I doubt it. How?'

'Obstructing the course of justice.'

'I hardly think so. I'm only trying to help.'

'I don't want your damned help.' The Inspector was spitting now. Bognor was aware of something damp striking him on the cheek. Possibly the piece of muesli. He dabbed at it with the blue and white handkerchief.

'There's no need to spit,' he said, 'nor to be so agitated. It would be much better to treat this as a team game. We're both on the same side.'

'Don't patronise me with your lah-di-dah public school rubbish. We are not on the same bloody side. As far as I am concerned, you're right in this up to here.' He made a waving

28

motion at his neck, hand only inches from Bognor's face.

Bognor backed off. 'Don't be absurd.'

'I'm not the one who's being absurd.' DCI Bumstead was obviously about to play an ace. 'I have reason to believe that at or about the time that Vernon Hemlock was murdered last night you were somewhere downstairs in this house despite having gone to bed. Or pretended to go to bed.'

'Don't be ridiculous,' said Bognor.

'Were you or weren't you?'

'Wasn't I or wasn't I what?'

'In bed with your wife?'

'Don't be impertinent.'

'I'm warning you, Bognor!'

Monica decided it was time to intervene with a little feminine reason.

'It's perfectly straightforward, Mr Bumstead,' she said. 'My husband stayed up a little later than I did. Shortly after coming to bed he felt thirsty and went downstairs to get some milk. He can't have been gone more than five minutes.'

'That's your story.'

'Yes.'

'If he was thirsty why didn't he drink tap water?'

'He doesn't like tap water, and I don't blame him. I've tried this Byfleet-next-the-Sea tap stuff and it's worse than London. And he's particularly partial to milk.'

Bumstead deflated a notch or two.

'It's a remarkable coincidence that your husband should choose to go downstairs at just the same time as Mr Hemlock was being murdered.'

'I don't suppose we yet know the precise moment of death,' said Monica, sounding knowledgeable, 'and I doubt the lab will be able to give you one anyway. And if you want further evidence I suggest you get your forensic people to check the kitchen fridge and milk bottles for prints. You'll find my husband's there. I was awake the entire time he was away and I assure you he was not gone more than five minutes. The whole thing is preposterous. Even if he had the opportunity to kill Hemlock what on earth would be the motive? And where on earth is your proof? It's barely even circumstantial.'

The DCI began to look uneasy.

'Anyway,' asked Bognor, 'who told you I was downstairs?'

'Never you mind,' said the policeman. 'The fact is that you were, and I find that in itself an extremely suspicious circumstance.'

'Do you just?'

'Yes, I do.'

They were squaring off again, Bumstead's face getting closer and closer to Bognor's, when the phone rang.

Monica answered.

'Yes,' she said, 'he's here. I'll pass you over.' She smiled glacially at Bumstead. 'It's for you. Your Chief Constable, I think the girl said.'

The conversation was rather like one between Bognor and Parkinson. In other words it would have been an exaggeration to say there were two sides in it.

What the Bognors heard was: 'Yes, sir', 'Yes, sir', 'No, sir', 'I'm afraid not, sir', 'Not at all co-operative, sir', 'Downright suspicious if you ask me, sir', 'No, sir, sorry, sir', 'Yes, sir', 'Is that an order, sir?', 'If you say so, sir', 'Under protest, sir', 'I understand, sir, and I'm sorry too, sir', 'Thank you very much, sir', 'I will indeed, sir'.

Bognor guessed he sounded like a bit of a creeper on the phone to his boss but never, surely, as creepy as that.

Bumstead returned the phone to Mrs Bognor.

'That was my boss,' he said, in a voice like freezing drizzle.

'Really?' Bognor realised his inflection was off-key but he could think of no other response.

'Your boss threatened my boss with a Q4.'

'Did he?'

'It's out of order. There's no issue of national security involved here.'

'We don't know that yet. Books are an international business. And they can get unpleasantly tied up with national security. Look at that fellow Wright in Tasmania. Books about MI5 and 6 are practically an industry within an industry.' Bognor tried to seem expert.

'I think that's just plain stupid,' said Bumstead. He sounded petulant. 'Anyway, my boss took the Q4 threat seriously.'

'So I gathered. Wise man.' Bognor smiled.

'That doesn't mean we have to co-operate,' said Bumstead. 'Just because you have or may have a Q4 doesn't oblige me to be on the same team.'

'It obliges you', said Bognor, quoting, '"not to withhold any evidence regarding the case nor to in any way impede the holder of the authority from making any enquiries howsoever conducted". Sounds pretty unequivocal to me.'

'It means', said Bumstead, 'that I can't stop you doing whatever you want and I have to tell you what you need to know. But it damn well doesn't oblige me to tell you anything voluntarily nor to abandon any suspicions I may entertain. You put a foot wrong, my friend, and I'll have your guts for garters.'

Bognor nodded.

'Good,' he said. 'Just so we understand one another.'

'Quite,' said the DCI, turning on his heel. He shut the door with a force marginally the right side of insulting and stomped off to do some more interrogating.

Simon and Monica listened to the retreating steps.

'Phew!' said Monica.

As predicted, the decisive move came from Milton Capstick. Bognor and his wife were drinking a dry sherry from their travelling decanter and speculating on the likely course of events when Capstick arrived in the nearest Capstick was ever likely to be to a lather of excitement.

'Look here,' he said, accepting a glass of Sandeman's best, 'can you pull rank on this really rather boring policeman? I have to present a paper at the RIL this evening. I can't conceivably duck out of it, sorry though I am about poor Hemlock. It's been arranged for months and it's completely sold out. One has a duty to one's public, don't you know?'

'RIL?' asked Bognor.

'Royal Institute of Letters,' said Capstick. 'It's immensely prestigious. Somewhere in Chelsea. I'm told Michael Holroyd's coming.'

'Goodness!' said Bognor.

'So you see my problem?'

'I don't understand,' said Bognor disingenuously; 'it'll only take three hours at the most to get to London. What's the problem?'

'It's that wretched inspector man. He's trying to insist we all stay put until he's solved the crime. Which will be for ever if you ask me. You must outrank him. Can't you order him? I'll be back tomorrow if he wants. If the sales conference is still on, that is. It's all too terribly tiresome.' He shot a cuff of Ariel white. His links were silver and coral of vaguely Spanish design.

'As I understand the law,' said Bognor, judiciously, 'you're entirely free to come and go as you please. You've not been charged with anything?'

'Most certainly not.' Capstick acted affronted.

'Nevertheless, you do seem to have been the last person to have seen Hemlock alive.'

'Don't *you* start,' said Capstick. 'I've had about as much as I can take from Bumstead.'

'It's true, though.'

'How should I know?' Capstick's Adam's apple was mesmerising. 'He might have seen all sorts of people after Warrington and I left him.'

'I understood Warrington left before you?'

'About thirty seconds.'

'So you didn't go down to the basement with Hemlock?'

'Certainly not. Not my sort of scene at all. Not at all. The idea of drooling over rude pictures with Vernon Hemlock. It's too horrible to contemplate.'

Bognor made a mental note or two and said 'I see.' Then he went on, 'No one liked Hemlock much, did they?'

'You could say that. He was bloody good at his job, though. And we all made a bob or two. I'm not complaining.'

'Even though he paid outrageously low royalties?'

'You're better off with five per cent of a few million than fifteen per cent of a few thousand.'

'I heard rumours about the film of *Looking After Number One*.'

32

'Rumours, what sort of rumours?' Capstick's Adam's apple rose and fell like a yo-yo.

'That Hemlock wanted Marlene Glopff to star and Arthur Green to write the script.'

'Maybe he did. I should worry. I had a good deal. Vernon controlled the rights. What he did with them was his affair.'

'So you had no reason to wish Vernon Hemlock dead?'

'None whatever. Am I free to go?'

'As far as I'm concerned, yes, absolutely. What are you talking about?'

'"Literature as Business",' said Capstick, 'subtitled "Combining Cash and Narrative Flow". It's about how to make money from writing books. Some of the Fellows of the Institute are absolutely hopeless at it. Famous and all that but they live off pitiful little bursaries and grants of one kind and another and they think marketing is something that happens once a week in Taunton and Dorchester. It's too sad.'

'How interesting,' said Bognor. 'As a matter of fact I'm researching something along those lines. Any chance Monica and I might be able to come along?'

Capstick seemed genuinely chuffed. 'Delighted, dear boy, and you too, Mrs Bognor. Can I offer you a lift? I have an idea some of the others were going to go as well. Vernon had laid on transport but I thought it would be easier and nicer if Ronald drove the Rolls. But will you have a word with Inspector Bumstead?'

Bognor said he would. It was not something he much wanted to do but needs must and he had one of his notorious hunches about the do at the RIL. It might just lead somewhere. They agreed to meet at lunch and Capstick went away to pack.

All Bognor's instincts in this case were the opposite of the police's. He recognised that part of this was to do with his personal hostility to the man in charge but there was more to it than that. The police instinct was to keep everyone under one roof, try to get some good forensic evidence at the same time as trying to trap people with relentless questioning to flush something out.

This might work but he was not optimistic about the forensic stuff. The fire would have made a fair old mess of poor Hemlock himself and would have destroyed anything else that might have come in useful. He supposed there might be fingerprints. The butler's, of course. Hastings might never have read a book but that wouldn't have prevented him from going down to have a private salivate over the pictures when his master was away. Dr Belgrave's dabs would be all over the place, too, since she was the onlie other begetter of the place. If there was any suggestion of Warrington or Capstick having been there that would be suggestive if not entirely damning. They had both denied making a visit the previous night. This might or might not be true but neither man struck Bognor as the sort who would deny something as incriminating as that if he thought there was any chance of some proof to the contrary emerging. The fact that they were the last two to be seen getting fuddled with Hemlock was bad enough anyway. Going to the blue basement library would not have made matters so very much worse. Either man could have said that he had stayed in the library and then gone to bed. That was not a murder confession. No more incriminating than Bognor's search for milk.

'By the way,' he said to his spouse, 'you needn't have perjured yourself. There was no need to say you'd been awake.'

'It made life simpler,' said Monica. 'Anyway, that's in the past. I don't think he's likely to resuscitate that episode unless you give him more reason for suspicion. And you're surely not going to do that?'

'No,' said Bognor, 'but who do you suppose told him I was downstairs?'

'The only people he'd seen were Dr Belgrave and Warrington.'

'But he'd scarcely had a chance to talk to Warrington. He'd only just left us.'

Monica sighed. It was time for lunch and she was worried that arrangements might not have been made. 'In any case, there are telephones in every room. Anyone at all could have rung to tip him off. After all, it could seem like vital evidence.'

'But whoever saw me was almost certainly the murderer.'

'Seems pretty likely,' said Monica. 'Naturally you didn't see whoever saw you?'

'Too busy looking for the milk,' conceded Bognor. 'Too much brandy. Anyway, why should I be looking for someone suspicious? I didn't know there'd been a murder.'

'It does have to be a murder, doesn't it?' Monica was musing.

Bognor nodded. 'He couldn't have activated those moving shelves if he was in between them. It had to be someone else.'

'I know,' said Monica. 'It's just that I feel there's something obvious we haven't noticed. Warrington, for instance, saying he went to bed before Capstick. Capstick saying they went at the same time.'

'*Cherchez la femme*, I say,' said Bognor.

Monica grinned.

It was almost a silent lunch. A cold collation had been arranged but no one apart from the Bognors had much appetite for it. Even Monica spurned the pressed tongue. Apart from 'I wonder if you'd very much mind passing the mustard?' and 'Could you possibly let me have the Perrier?', there were no exchanges of significance. The weather, television soaps and cricket were lightly touched on and quickly passed over. Before the meal began, Audrey Hemlock introduced a very grey man named Borage whom Bognor had never met nor even heard of. He was described as 'Group Managing Director' but his true status could be gauged from the fact that he was not a guest at Hemlocks but was putting up at the Goose and Goblet, a one-star AA pub opposite the railway station. It was no secret that Big Books was a one-man band. The only others allowed to play any instruments at all were Audrey, who had a fair amount to do with selling Big Books to foreigners, and Romany Flange, whose role really consisted of choreographer and ego-masseuse to the small élite group of Big Book millionaires. In Hemlock's lifetime Borage had been less influential than Hastings, the butler. Judging from his performance before lunch he would soon be returning to insignificance. Grey man, grey suit, grey countenance, he managed only a few grey words. These were, verbatim:

35

'My name is Charles Borage, Group Managing Director of Big Books PLC and Chairman of Aspen and Larch. Despite the appalling tragedy which has struck so suddenly, we at Big Books PLC and Aspen and Larch believe most firmly that the, er, show must go on and that our late founder and president would have wished it to do so. In view of recent tragic events, however, we will not be holding any sessions this afternoon but will recommence in the Winter Gardens as per usual tomorrow morning. I shall be issuing a revised schedule as soon as possible and you will be getting these along with the current catalogue which has been unavoidably held up at the printers. If any of you experience any problems with the media all that side of things is being handled by our Publicity Director, Chris Yardley. Thank you.'

He then exited left with Audrey. Chris Yardley, a retired Avon lady, was presumably fending off the world's press from the Winter Gardens, where she had a cubby-hole called a press office. You could tell what her status was from the fact that she didn't even rate the Goose and Goblet but was in a guest house on the promenade. (The Sea View. Prop. E. Wynne-Morgan (Mrs) 'Recommended. All Mod Con. TV in every room.') Any publicity worth the name was handled by Hemlock himself. Chris Yardley typed press releases, stalled Nigel Dempster and arranged occasional parties.

Paradoxically, the one absolutely taboo subject at the awkward lunch was the one topic that everyone wanted to discuss, namely the dead man and the cause of his death. You could feel him and it hovering over the feast like spectral ectoplasm, but something prevented any verbal expression of the common preoccupation – possibly the memory of Inspector Bumstead's dire threats but more likely that crippling English politeness which in extreme cases totally inhibits any expression of anything about anything except the weather and the cricket. Even Mr and Mrs Bognor felt so inhibited that they did not mutter between themselves but kept their heads down over the cold meats.

'Thank God for that!' said Bognor eventually, lighting a slim cheroot under the *porte-cochère*. 'Talk about funereal. Imagine giving us cold beetroot. I haven't seen cold beetroot since school. It would never have happened in Hemlock's day.'

'It's Hastings' revenge,' said Monica, turning up the collar of her Burberry against the salty wind which still spat at them from the other side of the pebbled beach. The gale put roses in her cheeks and a shine in her eye while blowing cigar smoke back in Bognor's face. She was still, he reflected, a fine-looking woman, while he . . . well, it was too late for recriminations. If you chose a high-cholesterol diet, sloth and gin you ended up looking like Bognor. Had he taken exercise and stuck to raw carrots, Malvern water and lentils, he might still look like Bumstead. Not that he'd ever looked quite like Bumstead, thank God, but one knew what one meant. A short life and a faintly disgusting one was what he had chosen and that was that . . .

'Hello there!' It was Capstick, dressed in a yellow oilskin with a curious rainproof fedora-style hat, the like of which neither Bognor had ever seen. In one arm he held the brown Vuitton valise with Cipriani label which was part of the essential equipment of seriously rich writers and in the other, less predictably, he held Romany Flange. For a moment Simon, who had marked Milton Capstick down as incorrigibly left handed, felt that sinking sensation he always had after a false diagnosis. Then, on looking again, he observed that Capstick was holding Miss Flange in what he could only describe as not a heterosexual way. He could not say in precisely what way this was so, but he knew it in his bones. At the same time he felt that something was up between them. Nothing sexual, but something all the same.

'You know Romany, of course.' Milton smiled, though not, of course, with his eyes. It was a determining characteristic of all Hemlock's big authors that they never smiled with their eyes. Nor did any of the characters in Big Books' fiction lists. It was a house rule. 'Romany asked if she could come along too. Thought she might learn a thing or two.' He lowered his voice for Bognor's benefit. 'I thought it best, between you and me, if she got away for a few hours. It's all been very upsetting for her and she is in a most delicate position, as I'm sure you'll understand.'

37

Bognor had formed only a fleeting impression of Ms Flange but he was absolutely positive that a delicate position was one thing she would never find herself in. Given Hemlock's known proclivities she might have found herself in some pretty exotic ones but delicate never. If ever a woman was hard as the five-inch copper nails Bognor used for murdering rogue sycamores or as tough as old Doc Martens, it was Romany Flange. Attractive, mind, if you lusted after women like sandpaper marinated in Tabasco, but not if your analogies were more floral. If autumn rose was what you had in mind then Monica was the head and Romany the stem. She had the longest magenta fingernails Bognor had ever seen. Her hair was jet black and so were her eyes. Her eyes were black as prunes. She had a definite look of that Conservative woman who told people in the North not to eat chip butties. Bognor could never remember politicians' names but he seemed to remember that the Conservative woman was proud of her legs. So was Romany Flange, and with reason. They were very good legs and she flashed them ceaselessly at any male worth attracting.

Her admirers said she could tell a Big Book by just sniffing at the first paragraph. Her detractors said she never progressed to paragraph two. Not even to sniff at.

'Absolutely!' said Bognor, trying to shuffle their elderly suitcase so that it was hidden under the skirts of his army-surplus overcoat. 'Delighted to have her along! Very sound move!'

'Good!' said Milton Capstick.

'Great!' said Romany, all girlish. 'Thanks awfully!'

The Royal Institute of Letters did not seem to have anything very royal about it, nor indeed institutional, if Bognor's sense that an institution was a large stuffy place with a pillared entrance and very old copies of *The Field* on glass-topped tables was correct. On the other hand it reeked of letters.

The Bognors had been dropped off at Baron's Court tube from which it was only one stop to Hammersmith and their new house, in one of the quieter streets near the Broadway. They were going to spend the night at home and rendezvous with

Ronald and the Roller next morning after breakfast. In deference to what he suspected would be the mood of the evening, Bognor changed his Apocrypha College tie for a suitably thick woolly Fabian number Monica had bought him from the Oxfam shop some Christmases earlier, and found an old corduroy jacket with leather patches at the elbows. Monica put on more sensible shoes and removed her blazer, substituting an old fawn cardy.

Arriving at the RIL they found that they were on the right tracks but just a touch too tweedy. This was clearly Eng.Lit. on the hoof but, though inclined to shabbiness, at least among the males, it was also surprisingly dark and in some instances even pinstripe suited. Not, Monica and Bognor agreed, *sotto voce*, that they were in any way Banker's or Advertising Man's pinstripes. They were much more like the pinstripes Bognor would have expected on the British Council's Representative in, say, Helsinki. He had only ever seen such suits *en masse* one night at the Tate when his old friend Fingest had asked him along for a private view. He guessed you wouldn't get a job at the Courtauld Institute unless you wore that sort of suit at the interview.

Several of the women wore just such fashionably high heels and just such nicely cut blazers as Monica had left behind at Hammersmith. There was the odd cardy and the occasional tweed skirt or kilt but generally speaking the women – who greatly outnumbered the males – were more expensively dressed than they would have expected.

'It's Public Lending Right wot dunnit,' said Monica, in a stage whisper, which earned her a very hostile stare from an immaculate dark suit with a pink, clever face and a mane of distinguished silver hair.

'Guests of Mr Capstick,' they said to the Eton-cropped woman on the door who looked at them with extreme suspicion.

'Mr Capstick hasn't put you down,' she said, frowning at the list in front of her. 'You're not press, are you?' But just as she said it another woman with the harassed, even mildly demented, air of a Lewis Carroll Queen, said, 'Yes, yes, it's quite all right,

Mr Capstick said he was inviting two guests, a Mr and Mrs Simon Bognor. That's quite all right! Do hurry along and whatever can have happened to Michael Holroyd, he's usually so reliable?' And she disappeared at a canter, clucking disapproval and saying something bothersome about dyslexia which Bognor didn't quite catch.

'It's upstairs,' said the ticket seller, looking happier now. 'There's a bar and you've still got time to order a drink if you'd like.'

Upstairs the men and women of letters thronged a minute bar and a not much larger lecture hall. Nearly all of them were drinking wine and nibbling pieces of cheese while talking at each other. It was very noticeable that hardly anyone was doing any listening.

The Bognors bought a couple of red wines from a small dimpled girl behind the bar who was dressed entirely in black and looked like a particularly gamine Italian peasant.

'Did you get the impression she was laughing at us?' asked Bognor, as they eased through the throng.

'Don't be so sensitive, darling,' said Monica, apologising profusely as she stood on the toe of a very small, dapper man with an equally small moustache. He accepted Monica's apology with a charm which seemed to Bognor to teeter dangerously on the brink of lechery. 'It's just that you look so much more like a writer than most of the writers. Anyway, I don't suppose she was laughing at you really. Remember what Inspector Bumstead said: "You're not half as funny as you think you are."'

'That's not funny,' said Bognor almost spilling wine on an important-looking dark suit of faintly Nordic appearance who was smiling distantly at one of the few men who looked almost as tweedy as Bognor. This person had very wild hair and a Shetland pullover. It was difficult to tell if the important suit was fantastically interested or fantastically bored. He was clearly an enigma, possibly even to himself.

'Look, isn't that Arthur Green?' Monica had to shout above the hubbub. 'Over there. He's talking to Miranda Howard. I mean Wilfred and Cynthia Midgely. Shall we go and say hello?'

Before they could do this a moth-eaten bearded aesthete of extreme pallor and restricted girth said, "Isn't it Simon Bognor? I published a poem of yours once in the school magazine. It began: "What price the holocaust of noon-day's sun in Brighton, now!" I've never forgotten it. Are you still writing poetry? I haven't seen any of your stuff.'

Bognor went very white.

'God!' he said. 'I . . . er . . .' But he was saved by the sudden advent of the woman who looked like a Lewis Carroll Queen who suddenly marched in grinning very broadly and clapping her hands. Behind her, looking rather sheepish but managing a smile of sorts was Milton Capstick, still in a blazer, clutching a clipboard to his chest and trying at one and the same time to appear terribly modest and fantastically successful. Behind him came an unappealing bald man of about fifty. He also wore a blazer but of a subtly different cut which Bognor tentatively identified as West Coast American. He also had an open-necked shirt with a gold chain underneath it. There seemed to be quite a lot of gold about his person. Gold at the wrist and on the fingers and, when he smiled, gold in the mouth too.

The two men sat down behind an insubstantial table while the fierce woman with the grin gave the microphone two or three crisp whacks with the flat of her hand, blew into it and said, 'Would everyone please sit down. We are about to begin.'

To Bognor's surprise everyone immediately made a dive for the nearest seat, including Simon and Monica.

'She must have been an officer in the ATS,' said Monica.

'I guess she runs a pony club,' said Bognor.

In seconds everyone was silent and the Queen said, 'We're very lucky to have with us tonight Dr Milton Capstick, who is to speak on the subject of "Business as Literature or Combining Cash and Narrative Flow".' Bognor was aware of strangled squeaks coming from Capstick. The Queen turned round and cupped her ear to Capstick's mouth. 'I'm sorry,' she said, giggling a little, '"Literature as Business", not "Business as Literature". And to chair tonight's meeting and introduce Dr Capstick I should like to introduce Mr Oberdorf Charles, the distinguished literary agent.'

'Ever heard of him?' Bognor whispered to his wife.

'Never,' she whispered back, 'but I'm glad he's not my agent.'

'I bet he'd make you pots of money.'

'At a price!'

The dapper, small man with the white moustache who seemed to have taken such a fancy to Monica turned round from the row in front and said 'Ssssh!' much more loudly than either Simon or Monica had been talking. Simon went puce and shut up and the small man winked at Monica as much as to say 'See you in the bar afterwards'.

'Friends,' said Oberdorf Charles in a sonorous Californian accent. The microphone let out a terrible ear-jangling shriek as if Mr Charles had mortally insulted it. Mr Charles hit it in the obvious belief that all it needed was firm handling. 'Fellow men and women of letters,' he continued, but the microphone had gone completely dead.

From the back of the hall a twin-set, jangling with pearls and drop earrings, called out: 'Kindly speak up, young man! We can't hear a word you're saying.'

Mr Charles did not look pleased at this. 'I can't hear a word you're saying either,' he shouted back.

'Thank you!' said the lady at the back, 'that's a great deal better.'

One of the RIL ladies advanced on the microphone and wrenched it like an osteopath dealing with a recalcitrant back. Suddenly her amplified voice could be heard quite clearly. 'Bloody thing!' she was saying. 'For pity's sake behave, now that we've got these monsters here.' She beamed at Mr Charles and signalled for him to continue.

'Fellow ladies and gentlemen of letters,' he said, 'it is my pleasant duty to introduce you to Dr Milton Capstick, one of our most successful men of letters, but before I do I want to pay tribute to one of the greatest of all British publishers who died so tragically last night. Ladies and gentlemen, I had known Vernon Hemlock . . .'

Bognor settled back into his chair and switched off. All around the hall there were idealised paintings of naked or partially clad ladies. They were not very well painted and only mildly erotic but he felt that on the whole Hemlock would have approved and considered this an appropriate place for a eulogy. He switched back on briefly to hear Charles say '. . . a man of integrity . . . a man of vision . . . above all a man of honour . . . ' and switched off again hurriedly. Most of the Hemlock authors seemed to be in the front row. He could see Arthur Green nodding in agreement. Next to him the Midgeleys. Their heads too were bobbing about like southern baptists in the middle of a particularly exhortatory sermon. The back of Warrington's head to their immediate left seemed less mobile as did that of Ann Belgrave. No sign of Marlene Glopff, who was presumably working out somewhere. This was hardly her scene. No sign either of Romany Flange. Capstick's driver, Ronald, had mumbled something about her being tied up and coming on later. Not like her to miss a Hemlock author on an occasion like this. This was just the sort of occasion she was paid to attend. Bognor opened half an ear again and closed it again when he heard '. . . selfless regard for his authors, nurturing, encouraging, praising . . . ' Presumably the eulogy would soon be over.

He got out his diary and scribbled on the page reserved for forward engagements for next year, 'Where Flange?' He passed it to Monica who looked peeved at being disturbed. She had either been having a good daydream or actually listening to Mr Charles banging on hypocritically about Hemlock.

After a quick craning of the neck Monica scribbled back: '*Pas ici!!*' and gave her husband the lofted eyebrow. Meanwhile, on stage, Oberdorf Charles had finished with Hemlock and was dealing with Capstick in similar though briefer terms. Bognor sensed an imminent peroration and sat up to listen.

'My friend and client Dr Capstick is, my friends, one of that rare breed who can transmute the basest raw materials into pure gold. When *The True Self* appeared five years ago it was recognised as a classic of its kind and translated into no less than seventy-three different languages. *Looking After Number One* may truly be described as one of the great books in this or any other language . . . '

'What language?!' called a voice from the back and there was a titter from the audience. Mr Charles ignored it. Bognor was dimly aware of a sense of well-bred irritation. Actually, on looking around and trying to pick up some vibes it was worse than irritation. The people of letters were, unless he was much mistaken, beginning to seethe a little.

'And in his latest and seminal work *The First Billion* Capstick has, literally, broken the bank. That book has become the bible of the aspiring self-helper from Brazil to Bangladesh.' Mr Charles's chain jangled as he warmed to his theme. 'Ladies and gentlemen,' he said, 'a very great British press baron once said that owning a television company was "a licence to print money". I realise that for very many of you, writing a book is a licence to *lose* money. But for Milton Capstick the art of authoring has always been what that great press lord said. Every time that Milton puts pen to paper – or, rather, ha ha, puts a finger to his wordprocessor – he is actually writing himself a substantial cheque. No man has done more to give writing the self-respect it deserves and so, ladies and gentlemen, I give you my very dear friend . . . Dr Milton Capstick.'

The applause was, thought both Bognors, distinctly tepid. But perhaps that was just the way one did things at the RIL. This was, as it were, Lord's Cricket Ground, not Yankee Stadium.

'Thank you, Obe,' said Capstick. 'Friends, fellow toilers in the vineyard of creative writing, I want you to know that when it comes to turning one's words into money one thing comes only second to having the creative genius in the first place – and that's having a good literary agent.'

No one moved. Some people might at this point have exuded a mild unease, adjusted the trim of their sails to catch a wind that showed signs of not blowing quite as one would have wished, but not Capstick. He might have an unequalled eye and ear for a worldwide audience in print but he wasn't quite so assured when it came to a couple of hundred in person.

There then followed his memorial tribute to Vernon Hemlock who came across as one of the great philanthropists of his time, a man dedicated to the pursuit of truth, of beauty, of friendship, of fraternity and – let's not beat about the bush –

44

yes, money. Bognor gave half an ear to this. It was rather like skimming the morning paper. He was able to do a tolerable précis of the contents while at the same time concentrating acceptably hard on the world about him. Thus he noticed Romany Flange's entrance, five sentences into Capstick's speech. It was a discreet but stylish entrance. She was wearing what Bognor took to be mink. She also appeared pink and flushed and over-excited, as if she had been running or possibly engaged in some other more sensual activity. Bognor had read in one of Dr Belgrave's works that it was always possible to tell if a woman had come straight from her lover's bed but Bognor's antennae were not all that well adjusted to that sort of thing.

'Money!' said Capstick. He had his hands firmly on the table before him and he now repeated the word several times, beaming at his audience and moving his head round the room so as to produce a semblance of eye contact with as many as possible. It was like watching a human lighthouse.

'There is no virtue in being poor,' he began. 'In fact any writer worth a damn has a duty to make as much money as he or she possibly can. And if the writer has an ounce of talent and an ounce of motivation and even half an ounce of audience awareness he or she will be a seriously rich person in no time at all. It happened to me.' And here he paused and did another sweep of his smile. 'And it can happen to you. And if it doesn't happen to you, quite frankly you'd be a sight better off doing something else altogether.'

Bognor winced. So did the man on his left. Monica glanced at him with a 'What in hell does he think he's doing?' expression. Capstick went on his way undeterred.

It was, in its way, a rather admirable performance, for it made no concession whatever to his audience or to the surroundings in which he found himself. Capstick must have known something about what to expect. It was no secret that the average English writer is a relatively impecunious figure – otherwise why had the Royal Institute of Letters asked Capstick along to talk to it? Answer: because Capstick was a phenomenon. Members of the RIL were almost by definition likely to be higher on pretension and lower on income than the average.

Indeed they almost certainly belonged to that dwindling minority of what Hemlock would have called 'arty-farty intellectuals' who saw a direct equation between artistic merit and popular indifference. These people wrote because of some bizarre compulsion or (another of Hemlock's cherished beliefs) because they were not capable of proper work. It was like a disease. Because they received scant financial reward for their efforts which went largely unread they convinced themselves that what they produced was too good for the vulgar populace – too difficult, too improving, too literate, too deeply meaningful. Once they had taken this position they had to accept the corollary which was that anybody who *did* appeal to the common herd was – by definition – vulgar, illiterate, boorish and philistine.

Capstick's first task, therefore, if he had wanted to be loved (which on the whole he did) should have been to convince the RIL that despite his vast international sales, his bulging Swiss bank account and his beautifully tailored blazer, he was, at bottom, embarrassed by all this. Naturally he would have been expected to advance a few useful tips about how serious Letters people might improve their material standards but he would be expected to do so from a position of self-avowed intellectual, moral and creative inferiority. It was one thing for him to admit to selling more copies and making more money but quite another to claim that his books were anything other than grossly inferior. Members of the RIL believed that they were the victims of a boorish, materialist, greedy society. They took comfort in the Reithian belief that they were nevertheless an élite. Their books did not sell and were not read because they were, in a nutshell, too bloody good. Their books, literature; Capstick's books, junk. They were certainly not going to take kindly to a man like him who came along to tell them that they were not only material failures but creatively second-rate, too.

Yet this was what Capstick did. Bognor did not follow his argument in every detail, not least because much of it was couched in the same impressive-sounding but ultimately opaque language of *Looking After Number One* and *The First Billion*. For example: 'Self advancement is fundamentally the apotheosis of the Yin' or 'Only by realising the true potential of self can one truly achieve one's goal: to grow is to grow'. The Bognor brow furrowed as he scribbled a few notes on key passages and he gave up completely when Capstick embarked on his famous anthropomorphic metaphors. 'In the warren the king rabbit will attract the greatest number of does by the simple expedient of . . .' or 'A single mating call from the sperm whale when broken up into an infinite number of micro-cells corresponds . . .' were ideas which seemed to Bognor to be effectively bereft of meaning. Yet the gist of Capstick's message came across loud and clear. What Capstick was actually saying in his forty minutes of apparent gobbledy-gook could best be summed by a word Oberdorf Charles was fond of using, though only in private.

'Arseholes!'

Although an increasing restiveness became apparent during his speech there were no interruptions or obvious manifestations of displeasure until he had finished. (One elderly gent with a silver-handled cane did walk out in the middle but evidently only to answer a call of nature because he reappeared in the middle of Capstick's dissertation on 'man as rabbit' or 'writer as rabbit'; Bognor was not sure which.

However, as soon as he had sat down and Oberdorf Charles had thanked him for 'that characteristically golden (smile, smile) piece of oratory', a forest of hands went up for questions.

The first was more by way of being a speech than a question and was from a thin woman with her hair tied severely close to her head. 'I don't want to seem to speak ill of the dead,' she began, 'but I have to say that I think the late Vernon Hemlock did more to damage the English language than any man this century. Speaking as someone who had the misfortune to have been an Author of Aspen and Larch's when Mr Hemlock took the firm over I can only say that if that's how Mr Hemlock believed a publisher should behave then we're better off without him.'

One or two members applauded at this but Mr Charles had risen to his feet, brow like thunder. 'I don't wish', he said, 'to comment on the gratuitous insensitivity, pettiness and downright

47

bad manners of that last remark,' (applause from the Big Book authors in the front row) 'but I would ask the questioner to ask a question and not merely make a statement. If she has no question I respectfully suggest she sit down and make way for someone who has.'

The angular lady did not seem in the least put out by this.

'My question is,' she said, with an almost gleeful menace, 'Would Dr Capstick's book have sold as many copies if it had been written in proper English?'

A noisy outbreak of clapping and even some cheering greeted this.

'Next question,' said Mr Charles, but Capstick was keen to make an answer.

'I would only say', he ventured, 'that at the last count, sixty-two point three-seven per cent of my total world sales are in foreign language versions of the book.' He grinned, feeling, evidently, that he had scored a bull's-eye. The front row clapped noisily.

'Then I only hope the translators had a better grasp of grammar and syntax than you have,' called the voice from the back.

'Next question; you, sir,' Mr Charles was pointing at the man who claimed to have published Bognor's schoolboy poem.

'It has been suggested,' he said, 'that the colossal sales of non-books like Mr Capstick's and others from the Hemlock stable actually damage the sale of proper books and prevent people reading. Would the speaker care to comment?'

'Whaddya mean, "non-books"?' Mr Charles showed signs of losing his rag. 'Each one of the Capstick books contains over one hundred thousand words. They have been recognised in every country in the globe. They have received encomia from the White House and from Number Ten Downing Street and from Mrs Mary Whitehouse. Dammit, if your sort of books were the only books, no one would read any more.'

Capstick was beginning to look ruffled. 'Each book', he said, 'goes through many different drafts. There is a degree of editorial input at every conceivable stage. One draft is always seen by a Professor of Linguistics who is a world expert in his field and whose advice is received with very real sympathy by all of us involved in the book's creation. I want the books to appeal to the sort of person who doesn't normally read books and I'm very careful to make them as accessible as possible to the non-reader.'

Bognor was slightly upset to note that several people, including their dapper friend in the row in front, laughed immoderately at this sally.

'You may not recognise it,' said Oberdorf Charles, 'but men like Hemlock and Capstick are creating The New Literature. Without them there'd be no books.'

The applause and counter-applause which greeted every remark was beginning to become uncomfortably adversarial. Bognor noticed one or two of the RIL officials becoming restive.

Now another voice intervened from the end of the row on which the Bognors were sitting. It belonged, Bognor realised, to a once-popular novelist, author of *Bladon Races* no less, now fallen on hard times and, at this moment, a little the worse for drink.

'I've 'ad enough,' he stormed in his once-famous Geordie accent. 'I thought it was a bloody outrage when I saw this feller 'ad been asked to come and talk but I decided I'd come and I'd give 'im 'benefit of 'doubt. Well, I've been and come and I've heard 'im out and I think it's even more of a bloody outrage than it were in 'first place!'

There was a storm of clapping. A cheer here and there, even a boo and possibly a hiss. In the front row Danvers Warrington had risen and was attempting to restore order. Bognor thought he caught '*aperçu*' and possibly '*bon mots*' but he could not be sure. The speaker had gone very white and was taking a drink of water. Oberdorf Charles, incandescent, was trying to fight his way through the throng to get at someone at the back – presumably the person who had thrown a sausage roll which scored a flakey hit on his exposed upper chest. Bognor thought he heard him shout 'Whingeing bastards'. It was impossible to be sure. Two of the RIL ladies advanced on the microphone which let out another of its banshee yells to add to the hubbub.

The author of *Bladon Races*, making an enthusiastic foray to the bar, tripped over someone's crutches and fell into the arms of the small girl in black who almost collapsed but was saved by another young girl with long blond ringlets.

Out of the corner of his eye Bognor saw that Romany Flange had grabbed hold of little Arthur Green and was leading him away by the elbow while talking eagerly into his right ear. Bognor smelt rats.

'See you later, darling,' he said to his wife who was on her feet like everyone else, savouring the full flavour of this clash of culture, this collision of art and artefact. He slipped away through the ranks of the Literati, all ready for the chase but sadly oblivious to the beady-eyed, athletic man in the leather jacket who had seen the departure of Romany Flange and Arthur Green, had watched Bognor go too and now, with a mean expression and a purposeful hitch of the collar, set off in a pursuit of his own.

It was cold outside, with bright stars in a cloudless night and not a cab to be seen. Bognor saw Flange and Green walking north up Radnor Walk towards the King's Road. It was no problem following them. There were very few people about and they never once looked behind, far too keen on each other's company. They were still talking. At least, Romany Flange was talking. Arthur Green seemed to be listening.

At the corner of the King's Road they hesitated for a moment. He hoped they weren't going to take a cab for he had a chronic aversion to leaping into London taxis and telling the driver to 'follow that cab'. It invariably meant disbelief which could only be dispelled by bribery by which time it was usually too late. In any case in his experience cabbies seemed very bad at following each other. At least once he thought he had executed the perfect chase only to find that they had been following the wrong taxi. 'All look bleeding alike to me, sunshine!' was the usual protest when he remonstrated.

There were more crowds now and Bognor quickened his pace, reducing the difference to about twenty yards as they passed the Duke of York's Barracks and a handful of punks in tartan mini-skirts and safety pins. He was perplexed by punks.

At Sloane Square there was another short hesitation by the taxi rank but then his quarries disappeared into the tube station. From the other side of the road Bognor saw them turn right for the westbound trains. As soon as they had disappeared down the stairs he hurried across the road and bought himself a 60p ticket and an *Evening Standard* to hide behind. Then he turned up his coat collar, sank his head into his chest and shuffled downstairs keeping close to the wall. Looking around he saw that they were sitting on a bench near the front end of the platform. He positioned himself outside the pub to the right and waited. The first train was for Ealing Broadway. Flange and Green did not catch it. Nor the next, for Wimbledon. The third was a Circle Line train and they ambled nonchalantly on to that.

Bognor waited until the last moment then sprung on and stood by the door. He did not notice a leather-coated man two coaches to the east who left his entry even later than Bognor, so much so that he only just squeezed between the rubbery jaws of the automatic sliding doors.

They did not leave the train at South Kensington, Gloucester Road or High Street Ken. At each stop Bognor lowered his newspaper just enough to be able to watch the doorway through which Flange and Green had entered. A stop further on, at Notting Hill Gate, the two finally left the train, still talking. Again Bognor followed as they climbed the stairs and left the station on the south side of the road.

From there they walked east, past the wine and food store, still open for late-night shoppers, across the lights, and on to Kensington Palace Gardens, otherwise known, like other plush London thoroughfares, as 'Millionaire's Row'. It was ill lit here, the road shrouded by tall trees, and Bognor eased back as they turned right. The crowds had thinned again. In fact there was hardly anybody around. It was a street of mansions, each one surrounded by walls and railings and the very latest security gear, for this one was embassy country and hostile embassies at that. The Czechs were here up at the north end; the Russians further down. Odd that the Communists should have set up shop cheek by jowl with Kensington Palace, home of Charles and Di, and Margaret, and poor Michael of Kent and his preposterous Austro-Australian bride. Thank God he wasn't a royal, thought Bognor, waiting for Flange and Green to be far enough away for him to follow discreetly. Thank God he wasn't a Russian diplomat, come to that.

It was really very dark just under the tree where Bognor was standing so he didn't see the man approach from the busy street just a few yards away. Nor did he hear him until he was a few feet off. He seemed to be about Bognor's height.

'Excuse me,' he said, 'but I wonder if I could trouble you for the time?' Bognor could not see the face at all clearly but was vaguely aware of a leather jacket and a faint smell of Gauloise and wine quite recently consumed.

'Er, hang on a second. I'll need to light a match.' Bognor's very old watch was not luminous. It had belonged to his father and was hopeless – unluminous, unwaterproof, unshockproof – but he persisted with it for old time's sake and out of filial piety. He struck the match and held it close to the dial, bending his head right down to try and figure out the numbers.

'I make it . . .' he said. But that was as far as he got. He was about to say 'ten-fifteen' but before he could say anything at all everything went both black and blank. It was a blow to the back of the neck, expertly delivered and guaranteed to put him out for quite a while. His assailant caught him before he fell, lowered him gently to the ground, then slipped away silently south towards the Palace.

He came round to find Monica staring down at him.

'Don't move,' she advised. 'You are perfectly all right. You are going to be better still but for the moment I don't advise you to move.'

Bognor turned his head. Not far, just enough to see if he could get his bearings and try to work out if he was (a) at home; (b) in hospital; (c) dead; or (d) dreaming.

'Aaaargh,' he moaned. Hearing his own voice, albeit from far away and in some distress, he decided that he could probably eliminate (c) and (d). It seemed to him, too, that in the split second before he had to close his eyes again he had noticed that peculiarly horrible yellow flowered wallpaper that the previous owners had put up in their bedroom. It certainly didn't look like curtain or plain Snowcem which is what he associated with hospitals.

'I'll get a doctor if you like but I don't think there's any need. You've got a lump the size of a baked potato behind your ear but your eyes look all right and your pulse is OK.'

'Don't shout!' said Bognor, 'I'm not deaf.'

'I couldn't wake you,' said Monica. 'I had to shout. You are a clot. You're too old to be knocked out cold and dumped on the doorstep.'

'Dumped on the doorstep?'

'Yes,' said Monica, 'you picked a real gentleman mugger.'

'What happened?' Bognor tried sitting up and thought better of it. 'God,' he said, 'I could use a drink.'

'You shouldn't,' said Monica. 'A nice warm drink. Horlicks or Ovaltine.'

'You know bloody well we don't keep Horlicks or Ovaltine. I need a stiff Scotch.'

'Tea,' said Monica, 'coffee if you insist.'

'I'm sorry, Monica, old biscuit, but honestly I'd feel a whole lot better if I had some alcohol coursing about the veins.'

'You shouldn't. You know what the rule book says.'

'You know I'm an exception to all known rules.'

Mrs Bognor gazed down at her man with a mixture of pride and concern.

'You are one prize gitto, Simon Bognor, and it's time you grew up.'

'Please, Monica . . . I really think I need that whisky quite badly.' He attempted a boyish smile which went horribly wrong but she succumbed all the same.

While she was fetching the drink Bognor tried to piece together what he could remember. There had been the evening at the RIL which disintegrated in chaos. Then he had followed Romany Flange and that rather pathetic Green creature as far as the entrance to Kensington Palace Gardens. He had waited until they had gone a little way down the road and while he was waiting this chap asked him the time. It was 10.15 he remembered but he didn't think he'd managed to tell him. He'd blacked out. Chap must have bopped him one when he was trying to work out the position of the hands on his watch. He fingered his bump. Quite expertly done.

'What time is it?' he asked Monica when she came back with a tray, bottle, jug and two glasses.

'About half-eleven.'

'Good grief!' He did manage to sit up this time. 'How in God's name did I get back here so fast?'

'I don't know,' said Monica, pouring stiff ones. 'At about ten-forty-five I got a call but there was nobody there. Then around half an hour later the doorbell went and when I opened the door there you were lying on the mat, snoring.'

'Snoring?'

'Well, breathing heavily if you prefer.'

'I see.' Bognor gulped, coughed and immediately felt a whole lot better. 'Did he take anything?' He was in shirt sleeves. His jacket was hanging, he saw, on a hook on the door. He nodded at it.

'I didn't check,' said Monica. 'Too busy worrying about you.' She was relieved. He hadn't looked at all good when she found him on the mat and she had seriously thought of sending for the doctor. Trouble was their own GP probably wouldn't have come out and then he would have fussed and finally he would have asked a lot of silly interfering questions and tried to make Bognor report it to the police. This last in particular was, she guessed, almost certainly quite the wrong thing to do. She could have asked the Board of Trade's man, Simcocks, but he was a rat and would have told Parkinson. Monica guessed that this was not something that should reach Parkinson's ears. Not yet, anyway.

She checked his wallet. 'Fifty-two pounds cash,' she said, 'driving licence, credit cards – various – photograph of your mum and photograph of me. You are soppy, I'd no idea you had that one, and it's ghastly. Makes me look like a retired weight-lifter.'

'Don't be silly. That all sounds in order. Keys still there?'

She rummaged. 'Keys still here.'

'Diary?'

'Yup,' she said.

'What about my ID card?'

'Yes. In with the credit cards.'

Bognor drank another soothing draft. His head ached, particularly where it was so bruised, but otherwise he felt in surprisingly good nick. 'The phone call was presumably him checking to see that you were in.'

'You think so?'

'Silly to go to all the trouble of dropping me off back home if there was no one in. I might have stayed on the doorstep all night. Died of hypothermia. Been remugged by someone altogether more lethal.' Bognor sighed. 'You didn't see anyone slip out of that meeting just after I did?'

Monica sipped and screwed up her nose and eyes. This indicated thoughtfulness and an attempt at recall.

'Sorry,' she said, 'I was too busy enjoying the show.'

'What happened?'

'Nothing much,' she giggled. 'The Hemlock contingent marched off in a state of dudgeon. Lots of writerish-looking people kept saying what an absolute disgrace the whole thing was and that nice little man I trod on bought me a drink and offered to see me home.'

'You declined?'

'I accepted the drink but said I could see myself home.'

'Dirty old man.'

'Not at all, he was a perfect gentleman.'

Bognor wondered if he might swing his feet off the bed and try standing. He thought better of it, however. If it was after 11.30 there was no reason to stand up. He told Monica the story in so far as he could remember it.

'That's interesting,' she said, when he'd finished. 'Audrey Hemlock rang about half an hour ago and wanted to talk to you.'

'What about?'

'Well,' Monica looked puzzled, 'I wasn't entirely clear. She sounded distressed. She said she'd found some papers and letters and things. She said she didn't want to show them to your policeman friend because she didn't trust him.'

'Didn't trust him?'

Monica put out a hand and soothed his fevered brow.

'Sorry,' she said, 'that's the wrong way to put it. She obviously thinks you're a superior intellect and would understand the significance of whatever it is she's found. The point is that apparently it's all tied up with Romany Flange and Arthur Green. There was some terrible row going on over Green's newest book. That's why the catalogue had got held up.'

'Say again,' said Bognor, 'only slowly. Not the bit about Bumstead being a dimwit, the bit about the row and Flange and Green. And I'll have a top-up.'

'You shouldn't. You're not well.' Monica made as if to remove the drinks but relented and poured him one. This was appreciably more modest than the last. 'Audrey wants to talk about it properly tomorrow but, as far as she can see, Arthur has been working on some book which will almost certainly infringe the Official Secrets Act. Romany gave him the go-ahead but when Hemlock got wind of it he went bananas and vetoed it. But by that time Green was well into it and Romany had seen a draft and she was so excited about it that she was threatening to take it elsewhere. Or something. Does that make sense?'

'Sort of,' said Bognor. 'You don't know exactly what it was about? Not third, fourth, fifth or whatever men we're down to now.'

'No.' Monica grinned broadly. 'That's what really does make it quite entertaining. Apparently it's called *The First Lady*.'

FOUR

They returned to Byfleet-next-the-Sea by train. The thought of
having to make some conversation with Capstick and Flange
during a long journey even in the Rolls Royce was too awful to
contemplate. Monica called Capstick's London number and
gave his secretary a distinctly lame apology. Her only consolation
was that Capstick probably didn't relish their company any
more than they did his. As for Romany Flange, who knew?
Questions would clearly have to be asked but not just yet. And
not in the back of Capstick's Roller.

The train journey was also fairly depressing to contemplate.
So-called InterCity as far as Bradleigh Parkway, where they
changed on to the local for the last forty-five minutes. The
InterCity's buffet was out of service due to 'operating diffi-
culties' and the train was forty minutes late at Bradleigh due to
'leaves on the line' and 'a points failure at Swindon'. Swindon
was more than a hundred miles from Bradleigh Parkway but a
points failure there was enough to throw the whole of British
Rail into a state of feral dementia.

Because of the delay they missed the connection at Bradleigh
Parkway, which at least meant they could get a beer and one of
the tastefully wrapped BR sandwiches while they waited.

'Tastes just the same as the old ones,' complained Bognor,
'only the cardboard's brown and they've chopped a gherkin into
it.'

'I can't open mine.' Monica tore at the clingfilm with her
fingernails. 'They must be wrapped in Spain.'

The Bognors had once had an entire self-catering holiday on
some Costa thrown into jeopardy on account of their inability
to cope with Spanish packaging.

'I wonder', said Bognor, 'how Bumstead's making out. I'd
like to talk to his forensic people if poss. Did you notice that
Warrington's bed hadn't been slept in?'

'You're just guessing, Simon.' Monica finally penetrated the package and let out a squawk of annoyance as she bit into the sandwich and mayonnaise sprayed all down her front.

'At least it's not Heinz,' she said, wiping it off with the paper napkin. 'I wonder if there are prawns in it as well. How few prawns before I can complain to the ombudsman or the Advertising Standards people?'

'Any prawn at all makes a prawn sandwich, I would guess,' said Bognor. 'I don't think Warrington slept in his own bed that night.'

'He's very fastidious,' said Monica. 'It's much more likely that he made it quite beautifully as soon as he got up. In any case, what are you expecting? Do you suppose the forensic people are going to put a toothcomb over every bed at Hemlock's to see if Danvers Warrington slept in it?'

'Well, no, I suppose not.' Bognor was not at his best. His head still throbbed and as so often happened in any case in which he became involved it got more difficult before it got easier. It was like the old canard about scandal. If you were to pick up the phone and call every number in the country with the simple words: 'All is discovered! Flee!', all the docks and airports would be jammed before breakfast. Same thing with the Hemlock murder. Before Vernon was done in no one suspected any of his authors of anything at all, certainly nothing to warrant police or prosecution. Now just because one man was dead everybody was under suspicion and skeletons were emerging from every cupboard in sight. Yet for all but the murderer himself nothing had changed. It was most unreasonable.

'Split a Cadbury's Fruit and Nut?' Bognor wanted something to take away the taste of gherkin.

'I don't somehow think Warrington did it,' said Monica. 'Even if you're right and he was carrying on with someone he shouldn't have been. I don't see a real motive there. Nor do I think he was being ripped off seriously enough. He's obviously doing fine financially. And he's famous. If it wasn't for Hemlock he'd be nowhere. Hemlock made him; Hemlock fed him; whatever he had Hemlock gave him again.'

They worried away at Warrington over the Fruit and Nut and then had a cup of filthy coffee from a kiosk while conducting another post-mortem of the night before. The most obvious first explanation was, of course, that Bognor had just been another statistic in the capital's grim mugging statistics for the year. But a mugger would have made off with cash, keys and credit cards unless a psychopath (impossible – the blow to Bognor's head was far too clinical) or unless he had been disturbed. If he had been disturbed he would hardly have managed to load Bognor into a car and get him back to the house in Hammersmith. And why go to such trouble to get him to safety?

'Mistaken identity?' mused Monica.

It was possible. His assailant could have assumed he was someone else in the dark. But it required a particularly guilty conscience to go to all the trouble of delivering him home. He must have felt very well disposed or fantastically guilty to bother with that. A positively Raffles-like piece of criminal chivalry.

And if the motive was not theft then what could it have been? The only possibility either of them could entertain was that there was some connection with Romany Flange and Arthur Green.

'Just suppose', said Bognor, 'that someone else at that RIL meeting was suspicious of Romany Flange and whatever plot she was hatching with Arthur Green. Now just suppose that person decided to follow them . . .'

'With you so far.' Another British Rail delay was announced on the crackling Tannoy. This was due to 'unavoidable circumstances' but BR very sweetly apologised for 'inconvenience to passengers'.

'Was that the Byfleet-next-the-Sea train?' asked Bognor, but Monica hadn't heard properly and the ticket collector he asked next just looked at him as if he was off his head.

They went back to their bench.

'So Mr X followed Flange and Green but found that he was actually following you following Flange and Green . . .' Monica nodded. 'Makes sense,' she said.

'And then,' said Bognor, wincing at the memory, 'he finally

decided that the only way he could get close to them was by eliminating me.'

'Simon, that's a good theory. But who was he?'

The station, one of the new BR efforts stuck out in the country in an effort to persuade people to 'Park 'n' Drive', was littered with other stranded travellers. They had the forlorn look of refugees with their down-at-heel suitcases, their string bags of oranges and chocolate biscuits and tartan thermoses full of strong sweet tea. Huge advertisements invited them to travel to Brussels and Paris in incomparable style and for incomparably low prices. But nothing told them how to get out of Bradleigh Parkway that desolate lunchtime.

The Bognors sighed in unison. Away in the distance a car door slammed and businesslike shoes clomped across the newly laid marble of the showpiece station. They watched idly as a long-haired man of about thirty strode into the middle of the forecourt and paused by the W. H. Smith bookstall. The man kicked an old Coke can irritably and peered round the station.

'Came to meet his old mum and she's missed the train,' said Simon.

'Train missed her more like,' said Monica. 'Hasn't been one for over half an hour.'

Suddenly the man's expression brightened and he began to walk towards them. Something about him triggered caution in Bognor's mind and he started to get to his feet.

'Monica!' he said. 'Don't look now, but I think I know this man. And I have a nasty hunch that he knows me.'

'Please don't get up, Mr Bognor.'

Leather jacket, thought Bognor. Leather jacket, old red wine, stale cheese, 10.15 in a dark street between the Czech and Soviet Embassies.

'Mrs Bognor.' The man inclined his head and smiled. He was good looking in a faintly Slavonic way with wispy fair hair, very high cheekbones, slanted brows and pale blue eyes. The eyes had the not inconsiderable virtue of looking as if they could be smiled with. A writer, guessed Bognor, but not a Hemlock man.

'Glatt,' he said, flashing a laminated card not unlike Bognor's Board of Trade number, 'Special Branch.'

'Not Merlin Glatt!' exclaimed Monica, '"The Dartington Rhymes", "Box", "New Year's Day, Richmond Ice Rink" – not *that* Glatt!?'

Glatt smiled with his mouth, keeping the eyes in neutral. 'I'm very flattered, Mrs Bognor. Yes, some of the time that Glatt. Today, "Glatt, Special Branch". Very occasionally, both at the same time.'

'Poets in Special Branch,' said Bognor sceptically. 'May I check that card?'

'Certainly.' Glatt handed him the plastic which Bognor scrutinised. He was unable to fault it.

'I'm extremely sorry about last night,' said Glatt.

'Likewise,' said Bognor.

'I'm on my way to Byfleet-next-the-Sea,' Glatt picked up the Bognors' case, 'and I have a car and driver. May I offer you a lift?'

'How did you know we were here?' asked Bognor.

Glatt laughed. 'I did say "Special Branch". To be honest I hadn't expected you to leave the house so early or I'd have driven you all the way. In the event I had to arrange some train delays. No problem there, luckily. It's amazing what half-baked excuses the travelling public will put up with. Even no excuse at all works perfectly well. Had to be done. I wanted to catch you before you had your interview with Audrey.'

'Audrey?! How did you know about Audrey?'

Glatt pulled a face. 'Come, come,' he said, 'you'd hardly expect our people not to check your phone calls under the circumstances. We're all on the same side, after all. No secrets between team-mates, surely?'

'As Blunt said to the Prime Minister.'

'Don't be like that, please. I really am very sorry about last night.'

'Quite a team,' said Monica. 'You, Simon and DCI Bumstead.'

'I agree. Mr Bumstead could be a nuisance. A great one for seeing things in black and white, by all accounts. Not a lot of grey matter. Lots of enthusiasm and self-importance and he's read all the books. Dangerous man to have on one's own side. Hop in.'

The car was an Anglo-Japanese job in dark blue, two years old and frayed at the edges. Anonymous from outside but quite sophisticated within. Reinforced windows, anti-terrorist devices, and above all a V-8 engine.

'Old crate can do 160,' said Glatt. 'I love it.'

He swung out of the station forecourt and lit himself a Gauloise, managing the manoeuvre with a dexterity which finally convinced Simon and Monica that he must indeed work for Special Branch or something similar.

'Right,' he said. 'Cards on table.'

'That would be nice,' said Bognor.

Glatt did not respond. 'You probably know I've signed a contract with Andover Strobe,' he said. 'Rude bestiary. That makes me persona non grata with Hemlocks except that I've been having a little thing with Romany Flange. Not that Miss Flange gives much away.' He spoke with feeling. 'Never known such monosyllabic pillow talk in my life.'

The countryside through which they were passing was very flat. Pretty villages with houses half timbered in white clapboard; squat Anglo-Saxon churches; pub signs swaying lightly in the drizzle. On a clear day the sky would have been an upturned bowl. Today the mist hung drab over vast fields of beet and the rain streaked the sides of buildings which wept from leaky guttering and high slanted roofs. Today there was no sky.

'In any case, Romany was also Hemlock's mistress as you no doubt know already. That put me even further out of court as far as the old man was concerned.'

He overtook a slow-moving baker's van and slid back in deftly, just avoiding a Spanish-registered artic which flashed its lights. Bognor bit his lip.

'Anyway, we got a tip just over two years ago that Arthur Green had got hold of some dodgy classified stuff and was working it up into some sort of factoid blockbuster.'

'Which was about the time you started romancing Romany Flange,' Monica said with a certain flat, feminist hostility.

'You can't have too many scruples if you work for Special,'

62

said Glatt, 'even if you're on the Literature Panel.'

Bognor supposed not. Sex with him had never been a weapon, though it had sometimes been an Achilles' heel.

'How much have you found out about Green's project?' he asked.

'Precious little,' said Glatt. 'In fact what Audrey Hemlock told you over the phone last night, Mrs Bognor, is about the best lead we've had so far. I was also able to confirm their major source last night. At least I think I was. Hemlock's murder has certainly speeded things up.'

'You think one of them killed Hemlock?'

'Neither know nor care,' said Glatt. 'From our point of view it's a mixed blessing. It seems he was keen not to publish Green's "First Woman" book. Quite why, I don't know. That suited us. We've had enough dirty washing in the last few years. British Security Services are already regarded as Comic Opera. Not that that's wholly detrimental. Being underestimated can be an advantage.'

They passed through a tiny hamlet called Miles Kington. A pub, a stores-cum-post office, a green with a tethered goat, pond with two white ducks, row of council houses, modest manor, old rectory, end of village. A signpost said Sheridan Morley 5, Byfleet-next-the-Sea 11.

'Major source,' Monica repeated.

'The Soviets,' said Glatt. 'I thought as much. Got fairly conclusive proof through Canadian contacts when I did a reading at Harbourfront in Toronto just after the PEN Congress in New York. But Green's been very circumspect up until now. He has contacts in our world of course. Always has done – just like all the others who write that sort of bestseller. But most of the contacts are superannuated old hacks who are way out of date. And most of the stuff is pure invention – even the best of it. Particularly the best of it. The reality's often dull beyond belief. But the buzz on this latest effort was that he'd got some real gen. Out of character. I know Romany was excited by it. She never said so but it was pretty obvious from the way she wasn't talking about it. You learn a lot from people's silences in this game. Like poetry.'

'You mean', said Bognor, 'that they actually went to the Russian Embassy last night?'

'Yes, sir!' Glatt shook his head in disbelief. 'Hemlock dying really has made them terribly cavalier all of a sudden. I assumed they were going there or to the Czechs as soon as they started moving east from Notting Hill Gate but I needed to be sure. That's why I had to get you out of my way. You were obstructing my vision. Sorry about that.'

Bognor felt any further comment superfluous.

'How did you enjoy the meeting?' asked Glatt, changing the subject.

Monica said she had found it hugely entertaining though she did feel that for the RIL to ask someone like Capstick was a bit off-beam, though on the other hand when all was said and done a book was a book was a book and letters were, as it were, indivisible. She described one or two individuals and Merlin was able to identify them, observing as he did that she had excellent powers of observation. This caused Bognor to prickle slightly but he wisely kept quiet. Glatt said that he himself was beginning to be worried. He had had a huge advance for the erotic bestiary from Strobe and there was talk of a Channel Four series based on the Richmond Ice Rink sequence. He was afraid this might damage his street cred. And while he wouldn't mind Capstick's cash he could do without Capstick's reputation. In any case he earned enough from poetry and espionage to live comfortably. He didn't want a yacht.

For the rest of the journey they talked shop and it gradually dawned on the Bognors that the apparently ludicrous idea of the poet as intelligence agent was entirely logical. There were literary precedents of course, especially in wartime. Graham Greene was the most obvious example. Latterly, Anthony Blunt had been the most obvious example of aesthete as agent: life outdoing literature. What self-respecting Deighton or Le Carré could have invented a master spy and double agent who was one of the world's greatest experts on Poussin (of all people) and latterly looked after the Queen's personal picture collection. Indeed was knighted by her for doing the job.

By contrast Glatt's double life seemed an example of

64

unusually good casting by the British Intelligence Establishment. The poetic renaissance meant that Glatt was asked to give readings at universities and polytechnics all over Britain. There were few more effective ways of infiltrating student society than as one of our most charismatic younger poets. He had read for South African miners and for Californian grape pickers and for Turkish Kurds – for dissidents the world over, not excluding Britain's own gays, blacks, unmarried mothers and primary school head teachers. And everywhere he went he kept his eyes and ears open. At international literary conferences and festivals he was a perpetual presence, seeming always to be in earnest confabulation with the likes of Günter Grass or Norman Mailer. He was an honoured guest in Belgrade and Budapest. He was invited to Soweto, though banned at the border. He delivered the Canaan Banana Inaugural Lecture in Harare and gave a memorable reading of 'The Dartington Rhymes' in Tashkent. He had been embraced by Fidel Castro.

Monica was keener on poetry than her husband and knew Glatt's work well. Bognor had never even read 'Box'.

On the outskirts of Byfleet-next-the-Sea he said he'd better drop the Bognors off by the railway station so that they could pretend to have come all the way by train. It wouldn't do to let anyone know that they had travelled down together or even that they knew each other at all. He was staying at the Goose and Goblet. He accepted that Borage, the Managing Director, would almost certainly recognise him but that was no great problem. His relationship with Romany Flange was an open secret. He had a reading at the Byfleet and District Poetry Society the day after tomorrow. ('Yes, it *was* arranged to coincide with the Big Books Sales Conference, and I agree that was mischievous but it was a chance to stay on with Romany for a day or two by the seaside. Besides, I *am* writing an epic called "Invasion 1940" so the sea is relevant right now.') There was, he thought, no need for anyone to be suspicious. He would watch from afar and in his own way. But he would like Simon to keep in touch. If anything drastic came up Bognor should simply call the Goose and Goblet and leave a message.

'What sort of message?'

'It depends what you want to say,' said Glatt.

'Oh, come on!' protested Bognor. 'I can't just ask the girl at the Goose and Goblet to say that Green and Flange have eloped to Moscow and I'm giving chase. Be reasonable.'

They were driving along the front, the waves crashing into the beach to their left sent spray across the windscreen so that he had to turn on the wipers.

'Just say something cryptic like "Tell Merlin Glatt there's a grating roar of pebbles on the beach".'

Monica purred.

'And if you can't get through to the Goose or you feel uneasy just call your man Parkinson and tell him to get Special to send out a Mayday for "Wizard" to RV with you.'

All this seemed a bit melodramatic to Bognor, but then everything about Merlin Glatt had been melodramatic ever since he'd bopped him one in Notting Hill Gate last night. Poetic licence, he supposed. Compared with the Board of Trade Special Investigations Department, Military Intelligence and Special Branch were still absurdly romantic and cloak and daggerish. But then compared with someone like Bumstead he supposed he cut a pretty Balkan figure. Well, perhaps that would be exaggerating. He'd always aspired to play an Anthony Hope hero but such hopes had gone the way of the century before lunch in the Lord's Test and the Nobel Peace Prize. Realism had, perforce, come early in Bognor's life.

'Shall we make a rendezvous anyway?' Monica had obviously taken a shine to the poet. 'You'll want to know what poor Audrey has to tell us.'

They were by the railway station now. Not much sign of life, but, according to Glatt, a train due in two minutes and likely to be on time. They could get a cab to Hemlocks once it was in.

'We could happen to bump into one another in the snug at the Goose around six-thirty,' Monica continued.

'What if Chris Yardley or Borage are there?'

'We can make it look . . . oh, you know, as if we hadn't met before . . .'

'OK,' said Glatt. 'Train's coming. I can hear it. I'll be in the bar of the Goose at six-thirty, but if I'm reading the new Gavin Ewart keep away. If I'm reading an evening paper you can ask if I've got the cricket score from Sydney.'

The train was approaching. Monica started to open the door.

'What shall I ask Audrey Hemlock?' asked Bognor. Something about Glatt was making him very edgy.

'Anything and everything,' said the poet. 'She can't tell us too much. Go on. We don't want anyone to see you leaving the car. See you later.'

'What an absolutely fascinating person!' said Monica, adjusting her headscarf and hoping that her back view didn't look too broad. The Burberry wasn't terribly flattering from behind. But then maybe Glatt wasn't looking.

Bognor growled. The back of his head was good reason for not thinking as highly of their new colleague as Monica.

'Bit of a poseur if you ask me,' he said.

A handful of bedraggled travellers were on the train. The Bognors mingled with them and hailed a cab from the rank.

'Hemlocks, please,' said Bognor, stowing the case in the boot, and then climbing in the back of the Ford Cortina alongside his wife.

'Hemlocks, you say?' The driver had the looks and demeanour of a bad-tempered potato.

'Yes, Hemlocks.'

'You don't mean the Winter Gardens?'

'No, I mean Hemlocks.'

'The Hemlocks meetings are at the Winter Gardens,' said the driver, who had still not even started the engine.

'I know that,' said Bognor, 'but my wife and I are staying at Hemlocks which is the private residence of the late Vernon and Mrs Hemlock. We are or rather were the personal guests of Mr Hemlock.'

The driver started his car with a noticeably bad grace and an air of some truculence. He had a large boil on the back of his neck, just below the greasy black hair line and just above the greasy black collar.

'Late Mrs Hemlock from what I hear,' he said.

'No,' said Monica, 'it was poor Mr Hemlock who died. In the fire.'

The driver turned on to the promenade and laughed. 'That were last night, missus,' he said. 'Seems poor Mrs Hemlock were so upset she killed herself this morning. Ambulance left with the body not half an hour ago.'

Their first inclination was disbelief but the taxi driver persisted.

'They were ever so close,' he said. 'Ever since they first came to Byfleet, well, must be nigh on twelve year or more, they were so close they were like two halves of a mussel. Folk remarked on it they did. Well 'tis no wonder she done 'erself in. Terrible thing for the town. Terrible.'

Bloody mutterer, Bognor thought, and prayed it was just gossip. As they pulled up under the porte-cochère, however, he had an uneasy sense that it was true. As he paid the driver Hastings came to the door. It was not the cheeky chappie of the day before yesterday, nor even the more subdued but still truculent one of yesterday.

'You'll have heard the news,' he said. 'Inspector says she killed herself, though God knows why. I'd have thought she'd be glad to be shot of him. Inspector's in the library. Expect he'd like a word. Expect you'd like a word yourself.'

'What's happening with the sales conference?'

'They're all down at the Winter Gardens,' said Hastings 'That creature Borage was saying "the show must go on", but I don't see how it can now. He's a busted flush.'

He really was chastened. He had even taken their case. 'I'll put this in your room,' he said, 'but we'll have to close the house up soon as we can.'

'Who succeeds?' asked Monica, trying to sound sympathetic. 'Were there children?'

'None,' said Hastings, 'that's just it. No one knows what's happening.'

'And Miss Flange?'

Hastings seemed torn between distress and anger.

'She's in the study now. Going through papers.'

Bognor was shocked. 'She mustn't do that. There could be evidence. Does DCI Bumstead know?'

Hastings looked truly miserable. 'No idea,' he said, 'but I've said more than enough. You'd better talk to him. He'd kill me if he knew I'd said this much. Will you both be in for dinner?'

'What's everyone else doing?'

'All dining in. Dinner as per usual. Miss Flange's instructions.'

'I see,' said Bognor.

Monica took off her Burberry and handed it to Hastings with her most ravishing and sympathetic smile. A combination of Nurse Bognor and Mata Bognor.

'Miss Flange is in charge?' she asked.

Hastings did not reply. 'Inspector's in the library,' he said. 'Dinner's eight for eight-thirty.'

'Dearie me,' said Bognor as they moved out of earshot. 'Below stairs is taking it very hard.'

'Don't be so insensitive. I'm upset too. Poor duck. She'd had a rotten life.'

They paused below what looked remarkably like a Bonington seascape: 'Schooner in Byfleet Bay'. It was noticeable that outside work and outside sex, Hemlock's taste had been subdued, discreet and on the whole surprisingly good. Audrey's influence, perhaps.

'Do you think she did it, though?' The schooner's bows were invisible in the swell. The artist, Bonington or not, had managed to capture just such conditions as still prevailed out of season in 'Breezy Byfleet'. Man against nature. You got a very strong sense of God's essential bloody-mindedness at the English seaside in November.

For once Monica had been credulous. 'I hadn't thought,' she said, 'I mean if they all say she killed herself, then . . . but no, I'd have thought she had more reason to kill herself before he was dead than after. But women are odd people, as you ought to know. She was very fond of him in a loony way. You think she was murdered too?'

'I'm keeping an open mind on the subject.' Bognor knocked on the library door.

'Yes? Come in.'

The Inspector sounded testy and on seeing the Bognors he looked testy, too.

'Oh, it's you,' he said, gracelessly, 'I was hoping you'd have stayed in London. We can manage perfectly well on our own down here, you know. You London people are all the same. Think anyone east of Limehouse and north of Watford has straw in their hair and paints themselves with woad. I don't suppose you know that when the Saskatchewan Police came over on their fact-finding mission last year they said that this was the most impressive force in the country.'

'Impressive?'

'Impressive.'

The DCI had turned the library into a working headquarters. Bognor wondered if it was described as an 'incident room'. He was not much good at police jargon. Jargon in general irritated him. DCI Bumstead had installed a computer, a coffee percolator and an attractive WPC who sat in one corner with an old manual Remington, looking busy, doing nothing. Pegboard had been stuck over most of the bookshelves, and maps, diagrams, photographs and computer printouts were stuck all over the pegboard. It was impressive in an irrelevant, bureaucratic and to Bognor very irritating fashion. It was rather like the British Rail sandwiches at Bradleigh Parkway. More attention had been paid to the packaging than the content. Symptom of the age.

'I gather', said Bognor, 'you've suffered another casualty.'

'Mrs Hemlock's passed on, if that's what you mean.' Bumstead fingered the moustache. His hatred of Bognor and all he stood for flickered across the room.

'What happened?'

'Overdose, if you must know.'

'I must.'

'My boss has had formal notification of the Q4,' he said, venomously, 'so if you must, you must. The doctor had prescribed sleeping pills. The packet was on the bedside table. Empty.'

'Suicide note?'

'Not that we've located at this moment in time.'

'Who found her?'

'Romany Flange.'

'Flange? But what time? Romany Flange was in London last night. I wouldn't have thought . . .'

'Evidently she and Arthur Green drove down here very early,' said DCI Bumstead, pleased to be able to surprise his unwanted team-mate with unexpected information. 'They got in before breakfast. Mrs Hemlock didn't put in an appearance at the meal. Ms' – he pronounced the unsatisfactory abbreviation as if it were simply an elision of 'em's and 'zed's – 'Mmmmmzzzz Flange went to her room to see if she was all right. She had business to discuss. I understand the business affairs of the company are complicated. Mr Hemlock tended to confide only in himself. There's a great deal that's not been written down.'

'So when Romany Flange went to Mrs Hemlock's bedroom she found her dead?'

'Affirmative.'

'Not comatose, but dead.'

'She couldn't find a pulse and when she held a mirror to her mouth there was no sign of any breathing.'

'So they rang for a doctor.'

'Naturally.'

'And you believe it was suicide?'

The Inspector was irritated.

'I see no reason not to.'

'She phoned my wife last night. She had something she wanted to tell me. We arranged to meet this morning.'

'So?'

'So it seems odd to make an urgent appointment for a few hours away and kill yourself before keeping it.'

'Suicide takes precedence over etiquette in my experience,' said the policeman. 'It's not something that's covered by Emily Post.'

Bognor had not thought Bumstead would be aware of Emily Post. 'You know what I mean,' he said testily. 'The only possible reason for her taking an overdose is that she was distressed by the death of her husband, yet we all know, don't we, that her husband was in the habit of sleeping with anything that moved? He treated her atrociously. She had every reason for wanting him dead.'

'There's no accounting for women, Mr Bognor.' He nodded in the direction of Monica. 'Present company excepted. Now if you'll excuse me I have work to do.'

'Me too,' said Bognor. 'I don't suppose your boys have found the papers she was talking about on the phone last night?'

'The scene-of-crime officers are making a thorough examination, Mr Bognor, and I've no doubt we shall have their findings in due course. But at this moment in time I'm not aware of any such papers. What exactly were they supposed to contain?'

'That's what I was hoping to find out when I talked to her.'

'Ah,' he said, sounding for all the world like a cut-price Parkinson. 'Well, I don't suppose you'll ever know, will you? It'll be one of life's unsolved mysteries.' And he stroked his moustache with the index finger of his right hand and he smiled.

The Winter Gardens were wintry but hardly botanical. The signs of summer were frayed and damp: 'A Viennese Whirl' with Edmund Gathorne and the Wellbeloveds; Arturo Grimaldi and his Italian Strings; Singalong with Verity Smith, star of *My Fair Lady* and *Cabaret*; Wee Georgie Jarrett and the Spangle Sisters. A dying palm tree bent before the prevailing wind and a string of coloured bulbs jangled above the foyer. The building itself was by Brighton Pavilion out of Jack Straw's Castle on Hampstead Heath – an Edwardian folly with a lot of what had once been white clapboard; a brace of minarets; a cupola surmounted by a weathervane of Old Father Time in a sou'wester; a profusion of stained glass. Nellie Melba had sung here once and – it was alleged – the Beatles in the days before their fame.

'Ye Gods!' said Bognor. 'Quel dump!'

Monica gave the taxi driver one pound fifty.

They showed their passes to the Big Books lackey on the door and passed through the foyer into the auditorium. The back rows of the stalls had been curtained off so that only a hundred or so seats were in use. These were occupied almost exclusively by men in dark, rather anonymous suits. The few women were better but still discreetly turned out.

There was a table on stage. Behind it sat the Midgelys and

Romany Flange, looking more sultry and witch-like than ever. Mrs Midgely – Cynthia – was dressed to kill. (Though quite what was difficult to imagine.) Her hair, heavily lacquered, was done up in what Bognor vaguely thought used to be called a 'beehive', and every time she moved her head enormous gold earrings crashed about like birdscarers. When she waved her hands, which was often, gold bangles jangled on her wrists. You couldn't see below her top but her top seemed to be composed almost entirely of gold spangles which caught the light from every angle and sent it lancing out into the far corners of the Winter Gardens, warming the cockles of the hearts of the representatives of Big Books PLC and spurring them on to sell just that final thousand copies of the '87 Royal Bedside Book which would send it into the top ten best-selling non-fiction titles of the year. By her side Wilfred looked merely dapper, in the same kind of suit as that worn by the reps, only expensive.

Behind them was an enormous screen onto which had been projected a stylised golden crown against a purple background. Under the crown, also in gold, were the words: 'Miranda Howard – World's Number One Royal Author.'

Bognor and his wife slipped into what must once have been the 'three and nines', picked up the Big Books Spring and Summer List of Forthcoming Titles, also decked out in 'prestigious' gold and purple. Cynthia was approaching the end of her spiel. She was telling an interminable and rather muddled story involving a television appearance with Terry Wogan and 'JR'. Someone had said that she and Wilfred were 'Princess Michael of Kent's Boswell'. Someone else had not known who Boswell was. Lurking in the undergrowth of this confusion was something Mrs Midgely had once found riotously funny but now neither she nor anyone else could think what it was.

Cynthia seemed to the Bognors to lose the thread and her audience more or less simultaneously. She sat down, clanking, to insipid applause. Outside, the wind shrieked. There were draughts in the Winter Gardens.

'Thank you, Miranda Howard,' said La Flange. She seemed extremely composed, especially as she must have needed a broomstick to get here in time to take the chair. It was only half

73

an hour ago that she was alleged to have been going through classified files at Hemlock Towers.

'One of the privileges of working at Big Books is that there is always someone of the calibre of Charles Borage to fall back on in a crisis,' she said. She beamed at the front row with all the warmth and affection of a frozen stoat and said, 'Thank you, Charles.' She rustled some papers. 'As you will already have heard, this company has been faced with a double tragedy, which is partly why I was delayed getting here for this afternoon's session.' A slight catch crept into her voice, and she paused to dab at her face. She could have been wiping away a tear or removing a piece of dandruff. You believe what you want to believe.

'As I said, I'm deeply grateful to Charles Borage for standing in for me and to Wilfred and Cynthia for carrying on so nobly when in their heart of hearts . . .' she paused again '. . . when in their heart of hearts they would probably rather have gone home and had a damned good cry. . . . Ladies and gentlemen, you know that to Vernon and Audrey Hemlock this company was one big happy family, united by a bond which meant much more than books or business.' She now reached in her handbag and pulled out a yellowing piece of newsprint. 'Ever since he wrote them,' she went on, 'I have carried these words wherever I go. They appeared in the *Daily Telegraph* and they are by a writer called Paul Johnson. You may not have heard of him since he is not a Big Book writer like Miranda Howard or Milton Capstick or Danvers Warrington, but what he says sums up a vital part of the Hemlock philosophy for he says that in Japan it is those firms which "embody the family image" which "have been at the heart of its economic miracle" because they give "the same sense of belonging".

'As I look around this great hall I feel, as Vernon and Audrey always did, that I am among family. That I belong. And as happens when any family suffers a bereavement, it mourns, it grieves, it remembers, but . . .' and here she gave a little half-smile '. . . it carries on.'

Publishing representatives are not universally or even widely remarked upon for their qualities of enthusiasm but this

74

provoked an extraordinary round of applause which, apparently spontaneously, turned into a standing ovation. It was not just the words. It was the image. The newly orphaned reps suddenly saw a chance of salvation in the figure that stood before them. Nanny. Bognor clocked the ovation at a full ninety seconds.

'I had my suspicions about her from the first,' he hissed at Monica. He had been uneasy about the woman before this speech. Doubly so now.

'She must have been coached by Saatchis,' Monica hissed back. 'It's not exactly Meryl Streep but it's not bad for the Winter Gardens, Byfleet.'

The applause died and the reps resumed their seats. Romany Flange called for questions.

The first came from a source that Bognor recognised but for which he was totally unprepared. When he had last known her some years before she had been of what might have been called a 'certain age'. Any doubts on this score were now resolved but she still had more presence – elegance, even – than anyone in the room except for Romany Flange herself. She was wearing a green tweed cape thrown about her in a series of twirls. Her complexion seemed whiter than Bognor remembered, heightened by the dangerous darkness under the eyes. On her head she wore a black velvet cap with a massive Victorian brooch where a General's badge would have been. Her eyes had the sort of mad lustre which Bognor associated with the drunk, the angry and the Irish.

'I should like to know', she said, 'if either of these two authors have ever met a single member of the Royal Family or exchanged a word with one?'

'It's Molly Mortimer,' said Bognor.

'Good question!' said Monica, 'but she doesn't look like a Big Books rep.'

'She's not. She's from the *Globe*. Shhh. This could be fun.'

Romany Flange obviously didn't like the question or the questioner.

'Who the hell are you?' she enquired, lip curling in a fair imitation of Royal at bay, run to ground by paparazzi. Even so did Prince Philip snarl at the World's Press every morning, driving his carriage out of the Sandringham gates before another day of bird slaughtering.

Molly Mortimer, however, was not one to quail.

'The question was,' she repeated, enunciating very deliberately as if speaking to a very backward child, '"Have either of the two authors on the platform ever met a member of the Royal Family?" And in case you think the question is a flippant or mischievous one I would like to say that over the years I have met all the members of the Royal Family and I'm sorry to say that I don't recognise any of them in the books written by Miranda Howard.'

There was a sharp, audible collective intake of breath. Someone – not one of the Bognors – tittered.

Wilfred Midgely spoke. 'It depends', he said, tentatively, 'what you mean by "met".'

The two women on stage ignored this feebleness and yet there was something about it which made Bognor give him the second glance which the little man normally never earned. He was the quintessential little man, especially when contrasted with the obvious Gorgon Medusas now flanking him. Yet as he sat, blinking out diffidently from behind his round, gold-rimmed spectacles, Bognor was suddenly struck by the sinisterness of the second rate. Crippen would have looked like that, he thought, and made a mental note to include Wilfred Midgely on his list of suspects if only for appearing so blandly unobvious.

'Are you an employee of this company?' Romany Flange rasped like a Black and Decker with a masonry bit between its teeth.

'I asked a perfectly good question,' said Molly, 'and I'd like an answer.'

Cynthia Midgely clanked into action like some superannuated battle-tank firing indiscriminately from every conceivable aperture. 'Any fool knows that writing about the Royal Family is an incredibly delicate and sensitive task,' she wittered. 'It would be sheer madness to reveal one's sources. Besides which, one has given one's word. One's whole credibility depends on absolute discretion.'

'Every word of yours that I've ever read is second rate and second hand,' said Molly, flinging a stray bit of cloak over her shoulder. 'The whole thing is just a monstrous hype.'

Bognor wondered why she was quite so cross. Everyone knew that she was telling the truth but it was a fairly stale bit of truth. Chris Yardley had appeared now and was trying to steer Molly in the direction of the exit. For a moment Bognor wondered if his old friend might not give the little Avon lady from the PR department a resounding biff with her shoulder bag. She was perfectly capable of doing it but apparently decided she had made enough of a scene for one day. The massed reps were oddly silent, never, presumably, having seen the emperor's clothes called in question quite so publicly. Certainly not during one of their own sales conferences. One didn't ask that sort of question at a sales conference. She whole object was to get everyone psyched up so that they could go and dump all over the opposition, not question the 'product'. The quality of the product was unquestionable. That had been one of Vernon Hemlock's first rules. 'Blind belief,' he sometimes told his sales force; 'blind belief is what sells Big Books. It's like Christianity. Think of yourself as a missionary. If you don't get the message across you end up in the pot. Your object is to make sure it's the guy from Penguin that ends up as stew.' Sales conferences were supposed to be like US presidential conventions or pre-match team talks in the dressing room. Molly Mortimer's interpolation had never been witnessed on such an occasion and the reps were therefore fazed into silence.

'Stay here,' said Bognor to his spouse. 'I'll be back in a jiffy.'

In the foyer he found Chris Yardley, composure fractured.

'She's press,' she snapped; 'so-called Literary Editor of the *Globe*. I gave her lunch at the White Tower last month. Pretty funny way of saying thank you.' She rubbed an imaginary speck from the lapel of her Jaegerish blazer.

'How did she get in?'

'Heaven knows. The goon on the gate must have been looking the other way.'

Bognor guessed the goon on the gate had probably nipped

out to the Goose and Goblet for an illicit pint or two in the snug.

'Where is she now?'

Chris jerked her head in the direction of the front.

'Out there somewhere,' she sighed. 'I suppose the rest of the pack will be here in no time. God, I hate the press.'

'They've got a job to do,' said Bognor sententiously. He rather liked journalists even though he disapproved enormously. 'Just smile and say "no comment",' he advised.

'You can do that with the provincials,' she said. 'They print the press releases without any silly questions. It's the Fleet Street people who are so ghastly. They never believe anything you tell them.'

'Tough,' he said. 'Must rush.' And he pushed out of the swing doors into the gathering, salt-licked gloom.

She was standing by the rail looking out to sea. On the horizon, south, south-east, the pale lemon gleam of the Toothpick light flashed spasmodically.

'Long time no see,' he said, conversationally.

'I saw you when you came in,' said Molly. 'Late as usual. You've put on weight.'

'It's age. Maturity,' he said. 'I didn't know you were the Literary Editor.'

'The *Globe*'s equivalent of the Sunset Home for distressed journos,' she said. 'You can say what you like about the *Globe* but you couldn't accuse it of being literary. It's hardly even literate.' She puffed on her extra-thin cheroot and blew blue smoke at the German coast. '"Big Book Tycoon Slain in Porn Basement Fire" – that's my paper's idea of a bookish story. "Dead Publishing Magnate's Wife in Overdose Riddle". Better still.' She shivered and pulled the cloak round her shoulders. 'A femme fatale like Flange doesn't come amiss. Pity Jeffrey Archer isn't a Big Book author but there are plenty of other household words. And the unmistakable niff of cooked books to give it real gourmet appeal. It's what my masters still call "a bloody good story", bless their little hearts.'

'What's wrong with the books?'

'I don't know. I don't understand accounts. Apparently our City boys had got wind of something. Hemlock had burned his

78

fingers in some American enterprise. Also the sales of some of
the alleged Big Books weren't all they were cracked up to be.
Anyway, what are *you* doing here? Don't tell me you're one of
Hemlock's authors?'

'In a manner of speaking,' said Bognor, huffily. 'Also the
Board are doing a report on publishing qua business.'

'Seems to me our City people were right. If you're sleuthing
around then there is something wrong with the books.'

'That's not necessarily a *sequitur*.' Bognor's eyes were
watering in the wind. 'But now I am here I'm investigating.
Naturally.'

'Got anything yet?' Molly grinned. All crow's feet and laugh
lines. She was getting to be seriously wrinkly.

'If I had I wouldn't tell you.'

'We could trade. We've done it before.' Miss Mortimer
winked. 'You know how discreet I can be about sources.'

'Like the Midgelys.'

'Those bloody Midgelys! The reason I flipped over them was
that I sent Hemlock an outline for a Royal Family Bedside
Book years ago when I was on the diary doing all those royal
stories.'

'And what happened?'

'Sweet FA. A flannelly rejection letter from Romany
Flange saying that Hemlock had passed on my suggestion and
she was afraid it wasn't "for us". Silly cow. The implication was
that I was an impertinent half-wit and how could any sane
person imagine that people would hand over real money for a
book like that. I think she said it would make a perfectly
acceptable series for the *Globe* but that there was more to a
book than just rehashing a lot of newspaper articles. Then a
year later out came this Miranda Howard book based on my
ideas.'

'Did you sue?'

Molly laughed and shrugged. 'God, it's cold,' she said. 'I'm
going to phone the office. No, of course I didn't sue. All the
barristers I know are rich enough already.'

Back in the Winter Gardens equilibrium had been restored.

The Midgelys and Romany Flange were showing slides of members of the Royal Family in different sorts of funny hats. Reps laughed dutifully.

'Anything happen?' Bognor asked.

Monica wrinkled her nose. 'It's all rather yukky actually,' she said. 'I feel rather sorry for the poor Royals for the first time in my life. Imagine being written about by two complete strangers – especially those two.'

Bognor told her about Molly Mortimer's experience of being ripped off.

'Can't say it surprises me,' said Monica. 'No copyright in an idea. Isn't that what they say?'

'It still makes the Midgelys a pair of perfect shysters,' said Bognor.

'Not necessarily,' said Monica. 'They need never have known. All that happens is that Vernon Hemlock calls them up and says "Guys, I've got this great idea for your next bestseller." That way they're indebted to him. Bet you it's reflected in the deal they did, too. *The Royal Bedside Book* by Miranda Howard, from an original idea by Vernon Hemlock."'

'Ha!' said Bognor. 'Is there a murder motive lurking in there?'

'Not that I can see,' said Monica.

It was teatime. The last of the funny-hatted royal pictures faded from the screen and Romany Flange announced that they would break for half an hour before Arthur Green talked to them about his new book, *The First Lady*. She must emphasise – especially in view of the earlier incursion by the press – that what he was going to say was highly confidential. So would people please be extra-specially careful to report anyone they didn't recognise and also not to talk about what Mr Green had to say outside the hall.

The Bognors mingled but made a point of mingling in the direction of Romany Flange. Both the Midgelys and Arthur Green were under siege, surrounded by swarms of reps. Romany Flange hovered on the fringe ready to pounce on any impropriety or rocking of the boat. The atmosphere was subdued.

'I understand you and Arthur Green drove down early this morning,' said Simon, conversationally.

'Yes,' she said; 'there was so much to do and then, of course, poor Audrey.'

'Poor Audrey. Yes.'

They all sipped tea. It was very strong and Indian and served from old chipped caterers' urns. There were paste sandwiches, too. And buns, chocolate, heavy on the flour.

'You and Audrey . . .' said Bognor. He was toying with a bun. 'Did you . . . that is . . .'

'What Simon means', said Monica, 'is that there was no very obvious reason for any love being lost between you and Audrey.'

'Your husband would be absolutely correct,' said Romany Flange, 'though I should have thought this was hardly the time or place to point it out.'

'You mean', Bognor had taken a substantial bite from the bun so that his voice was thick and indistinct, 'there was no reason for you to like Mrs Hemlock? Or do you mean that you didn't like Mrs Hemlock?'

'What exactly are you suggesting?'

Bognor smiled and swallowed hard. 'Just that you didn't care for her. And that there were good reasons for it.'

'Meaning?'

'That you were sleeping with Mrs Hemlock's husband and doing your level best to get control of the company she had helped him start.'

'With respect,' said Ms Flange coolly, 'that's more of a reason for her to dislike me than for me to dislike her.'

'You mean you did like her?'

'I had no strong feelings one way or the other.' She watched Bognor gagging himself with another mouthful. 'And now if you'll excuse me I must circulate before the next session. I have work to do.'

The Bognors watched her smoulder off.

'I'm impressed,' said Monica. 'Not someone I'd have in the house, but if you're talking about survival of the fittest she's my man.'

'Not a lady in the accepted sense?'

'Correct. She and Merlin Glatt are supposed to be having a bit of a ding-dong. What are we supposed to make of that?'

'You tell me,' said Bognor.

Monica raised an eyebrow. 'I think we'll ask Merlin Glatt to tell us what to make of that. Working for Special Branch is all very well but there is a limit.'

The bells were ringing. It was time for Arthur Green.

Whereas the Midgely performance had been so much well-oiled flannel this was as near to the Real McCoy as Bognor guessed a Big Book presentation ever came. If anything it was enhanced by the fact that whatever Mr Green's virtues, self-promotion was not one of them. Arthur Green was one of the least noticeable people you could meet. In fact his run-of-the-mill, humdrum ordinariness was so unremarkable that it almost became bizarre. There was nothing memorable about him at all. His features, his clothing, his speech, his manner were all so determinedly neutral that even if you spent months locked up with him in a padded cell you would remember nothing whatever about him the moment you were released. He was an unperson – a living blancmange.

But he had a good story.

The fact that the story was told by this anonymous figure in this anonymous voice meant that nothing distracted you from it. True, Cynthia Midgely had nothing to say but, even if she had, that clanking jewellery and over-elaborate coiffeur would have got in its way. Arthur Green was a throw-back to the pre-Mcluhan era. In his case the message was the message and the message was riveting.

It was a spy story and like all British spy stories since the war it began in Cambridge in the shadowy, élitist bisexual world inhabited by Blunt, Burgess and Maclean. Green sketched in the familiar background – arrogant cloistered youth shaken rigid by the Fascist threat of Hitler's Germany and ill-disposed to the sort of narrow patriotism that had made it possible. It was a generation that did not believe in country right or wrong, would not fight for King and country and agreed passionately with E. M. Forster that personal friendship was more important than anything else.

Although it was old stuff Bognor had to concede that Green told it quite beautifully. He had that elusive gift which often makes stylistically second-rate authors into bestsellers. It was not so much the ability to tell a story as the ability to hold an audience, to keep a reader turning the page because he was anxious to know what happened on the other side.

From Cambridge and the Apostles, Green continued with the well known traitors' tale. He followed them into Foreign Office, Intelligence, the Queen's Picture Gallery, the very heart of the British Establishment and, ultimately, in the case of Burgess, Maclean and Philby, to Moscow itself. He discussed Blunt, speculated on Sir Roger Hollis who, on balance, he considered too stupid to have been a double agent and ran through the famous Australian case when the Government tried to ban the publication of a kiss-and-tell volume by one of its former 'spy catchers'. Looking round the hall Bognor was fascinated to see that the reps were utterly engrossed. It was almost as if they had been hypnotised. They sat with their mouths ajar nodding slightly in time to the words. Bognor had never before seen such a powerful visual demonstration of the word 'agog'.

Nevertheless there was no novelty in it for the first quarter of an hour. It was a brilliant piece of précis but it was still a plagiarised précis, a fact which, just at the right moment, Green himself acknowledged. There was, he said, a school of thought that a line had been written under the story of the Cambridge traitors, that we knew all we ever would know. Some experts still drivelled on about fifth, sixth, seventh men. Lord Rothschild had had to write to the *Daily Telegraph* to clear his name. Just because so many of the principals were homosexually inclined everyone went searching for more men. Nobody uttered those famous words: 'Cherchez la femme.'

The rest of the Green story was brand new and so red-hot that even now he wasn't giving away every last detail. Ever since Burgess and Maclean had done their celebrated cross-Channel bunk in 1951 a whole host of official and unofficial investigators had been ferreting around the story to see how far the conspiracy extended and if possible to determine whether there had been a mastermind behind it. Now, as the result of many years of research, he, Arthur Green, was in a position to reveal that the whole plot was the work of one of the most famous of all Cambridge philosophers, a pioneer feminist whose name he was not prepared, even here among friends and colleagues, to reveal, until publication day itself.

The reps might not have been able to work it out from the clues that followed but Monica could and did.

'Daisy Butskell-Godunov,' she scribbled on the fly-leaf of her *Good Housekeeping* Diary.

Bognor nodded as if he had guessed as much all along.

Daisy's origins had always been mysterious – rather like those of her friend and contemporary Brendan Bracken. Somehow or other Green seemed to have got hold of some of her confidential papers, including diaries. He was fudging the story, trying to whet the reps' appetites without running too many risks, so he was being vaguer than he would presumably be when it came to cold print. According to him Daisy had been born a Russian Princess in 1901 and sent to English boarding school in 1914. She was there when her family were wiped out three years later by the Bolsheviks.

After that she had been passed around, like a parcel, among friends and distant relations but by the time she arrived in Cambridge just after the war she was quite independent. Formidably intelligent, stunningly beautiful, she knew everyone from Keynes and Wittgenstein to Noël Coward and Ivor Novello. Naturally her background gave her the reputation of being passionately anti-Communist. Indeed her name was linked – and not just intellectually – with that of Oswald Mosley but Green's new discoveries among her papers revealed that this was a pose. She appeared to have contacts with exiled members of the revolutionary left from her earliest teens. In the twenties and thirties she made at least three clandestine trips to Soviet Russia where she almost certainly had a brief romantic liaison with Stalin himself. (Green was prepared to claim that she was the only woman who had had carnal knowledge of both Stalin and Churchill.)

Although barred by sex from membership of the Apostles she

was the nearest thing to an Honorary Female Member that that preposterous society admitted. She apparently got to know Philby through his father, St John Philby, the celebrated Arabist. From then on she was away. She recruited them; she ran them; and she recruited and ran literally hundreds of other bright young Cambridge traitors throughout her life. She was still Moscow's most significant British subject when she died in 1967, victim of a never-explained hit-and-run motor accident outside her London flat in Dilke Street, Chelsea. She was laden with honours – an honorary fellowship of her college, a governorship of the BBC, a life peerage. There had never been a whisper of public suspicion; precious few in private.

Green ended by saying that many of Daisy's stooges were still in place. They were often in positions of importance and sensitivity. Cabinet. The Synod. The Committee of MCC. In the book he would be naming names.

'Hmmm,' said Bognor, as Green sat down to a silence which slowly turned into a thoughtful rather than rapturous applause. 'Interesting.'

'Very.' Monica, if not quite agog, still looked distinctly thoughtful. 'Do you believe it?'

Bognor sighed. 'It sounds a bit like a case of the factoids,' he said.

'But he's treating it as real history,' said Monica. 'It's not one of those "This-is-a-true-story-but-I-have-changed-one-or-two-details-and-called-it-a-novel-so-none-of-the-bastards-can-sue" books.'

'What the BBC calls a "docu-drama",' said Bognor. 'No, it sounds as if Arthur's breaking new ground.'

'And he's got these papers. I wonder if they can prove they're genuine.'

Bognor laughed without a lot of humour. 'They'll wheel out some "expert" like poor Hugh Trevor-Roper,' he said.

'And then Daisy's friends will roll out another expert who'll say the opposite.'

'All good for sales,' said Bognor. 'Nothing like "fake, says expert" to create interest in a new book.'

'And what's it all got to do with last night?'

Bognor frowned. 'Are we to assume the two of them had a rendezvous at eighteen Kensington Park Gardens?'

'The Soviet Embassy?'

'Exactly.'

'That's obviously where Glatt saw them go in.'

'My guess too. Now why would Green and Flange beat it straight to the Soviet Embassy as soon as Hemlock kicks the bucket?'

'And why', mused Monica, 'should poor Audrey pass on the next morning?'

'Coincidence has to be the most likely answer,' said Bognor, 'statistically speaking. I wonder if Green got his information from the Soviets?'

The Winter Gardens were emptying now. Green had explained with a sorrowful smile that in view of the sensitive nature of his material he couldn't entertain questions. The reps were scurrying off. It wasn't opening time yet so any alcohol would have to be in the privacy of hotel rooms. Bognor guessed the score. Scotch from plastic toothmugs; wine from the box.

'What's *The First Lady* got to do with the murder? With the murders?' Monica flipped her scarf over her shoulder.

'Plural?'

'I think so.' Bognor stood. 'I wish I was at home,' he said. 'I feel assailed – deaths, motives, opportunities, they do so pile in on one.'

'Nature of the beast,' said his wife. 'It's ever thus. You know that. Call Everyman and say "Flee – all is discovered" and there wouldn't be a man left in the country. They'd all be on the night mail with Burgess and Maclean. Mankind is a guilty secret waiting to be found out.'

'What cynicism and profundity!'

'Pouf!' Monica darted an unexpected kiss on Bognor's pink and stubbly cheek. 'True, though,' she said.

They left the darkling Winter Gardens arms linked. A pink fairy light about to fuse winked from the string above the portico. The wind had dropped and a sea mist burgeoned.

'I'd like a candy floss or a stick of Byfleet rock,' said Bognor.

'You've only just had a chocolate bun.'

'I want to take away the taste.'

They walked along the front.

'Look!' Bognor waved a hand into the damp grey yonder. A single illuminated shop-front shone out from an otherwise dark parade. 'Marine Ice Cream Parlour. Prop. F. Mozzarella.'

'It's open,' he said.

'Must be a CIA front,' said Monica. 'No sane man would open an ice cream parlour at the seaside on a day like this.'

'I wonder if they'd do a knickerbocker glory.'

'You're not serious.'

'Never more so.'

They paused for a moment in front of the window. There was a marvellously lurid display of sundaes in fussy glass dishes and bowls and flutes. They were like something from a Victorian doll's house only life size. Peering over this and into the café Bognor saw gingham check tables at which no one sat, also a stout man in an apron. He was standing at the counter watching a small television. Presumably Prop. F. Mozzarella watching an Australian soap opera.

As they entered, a bell over the door jangled, causing Mr Mozzarella to look up. He did not look very pleased to see them.

'You are open?' Monica spoke tentatively.

Mr Mozzarella nodded, and indicated a table by the window.

'I'd just like a cup of tea,' said Monica. 'My husband wants a knickerbocker glory.'

Mr Mozzarella looked at Bognor. Monica looked at Simon. Simon grinned, shifted his weight from one foot to the other and rubbed the back of his neck. 'Or a banana split if knickerbocker glory's off,' he said helpfully.

'Knickerbocker glory is on if you want it.'

'Terrific.'

They sat.

'He was a bad man, Hemlock,' said Monica, pushing the pepper shaker against the plastic tomato which contained ketchup. 'Could he have been killed because of Green's book?'

Bognor picked at congealed ketchup with the prongs of his fork. 'It seems to me that he wasn't going to publish it.'

'Why not? It's a good story.'

'If true.'

'That never bothered him in the past. He never let the truth interfere with a good story.'

'Maybe the Government had asked him not to,' said Bognor. 'Maybe they'd bribed him. An honour. He'd have liked a "K". *Sir* Vernon would have appealed to him.'

'Don't spill the beans and you get a knighthood.'

'Stranger things have happened.'

'But Green could just have taken the book elsewhere.'

Bognor smiled a superior smile. 'Not if I know anything about the way Hemlock drafted his contracts. You're thinking he might have offered it to Andover Strobe.'

'It had crossed my mind,' conceded Monica.

'What I want to know', said Bognor, 'is why the Russian Embassy? If it was the Russian Embassy.'

'Maybe it's a Russian propaganda ploy.'

'It would follow. The whole saga from Blunt onwards has always looked like a well orchestrated plot by Comrade General Philby if you ask me.'

Mr Mozzarella had disappeared from view behind a curtain of beads. He now emerged bearing a tray with a black teapot, white cup and saucer and a dazzling multicoloured kaleidoscope of fruit and ice cream set in a sundae glass and topped with a miniature parasol. The shaft of this speared two maraschino cherries to a sphere of Cornish Dairy Cream sprinkled with chocolate chips and hundreds and thousands.

'Oh, Simon,' said Monica, 'you're disgusting.'

As she said it the door jangled again and a small figure in a rakish sou'wester and Barbour half fell into the café together with a blast of damp Arctic air. The wind had freshened.

'Thank God you're here,' said Dr Belgrave, wiping her eyes and starting to remove the coat. 'I thought I must have lost you.'

She stared at Bognor's ice cream. 'That bloody Flange wants a Condom Cook Book in aid of AIDSAID,' she said. 'That looks like the front cover. I'll have a tea, please.'

She blew on her hands, rubbing them together.

'This Green book's a bugger,' she said, 'no getting away from it. And I'm afraid it's the key to the whole sordid business.'

'I'm sorry,' said Bognor, delving into his knickerbocker glory with the long spoon provided by Mr Mozzarella. The length of the spoon made him think of supping with the devil and he gave Dr Belgrave a sharp, uncomfortable look. How sinister was she? She was bad looking certainly, but you couldn't convict on appearance and some of the nicest people Bognor had ever known were perfectly hideous. Male mainly, it was true. Come to think of it he was no oil painting himself. The knickerbocker glory was what a certain class of gastronomic journalist called a 'revelation'. 'Sinful', too, though that was a different school of gastro-journalism.

'How do you mean?' he asked. He had forgotten how much he liked maraschino cherries.

'It must be why poor Vernon was murdered. Audrey, too.'

Mr Mozzarella arrived with another cup and saucer.

'When you want another pot just give us a shout, darling,' he said to Dr Belgrave. He did not have an Italian accent.

'Why should the Hemlocks be murdered on account of Green's new book?' Bognor decided, not for the first time, that obtuseness was the best tactic to employ.

'It's a long story,' said Dr Belgrave. She took her tea black and unsugared. 'And one I hoped I'd never have to tell.'

'I'm going to have to hear it, though,' thought Bognor. Out loud he said, 'Perhaps you'd better start at the beginning.'

'I first met Daisy at Girton,' she said. 'She really was rather wonderful. I think all my year were a little bit in love with her. It wasn't just her looks or her brains, there was something you very seldom encounter in my experience – a vitality, an exuberance, an optimism. You felt when you were with Daisy that anything was possible. And with Daisy it damn near always was.'

Dr Belgrave paused. She seemed distressed, on the verge of a self-revelation she knew that she would regret. Both Bognors smiled, seeking to encourage.

'I was a star pupil,' she said. 'Teacher's pet. She took me up. There was a villa in Fiesole one summer vac. A reading party.

The year after, a lodge in the Highlands. Bloody rain. And Daisy liked to golf. It would have been purgatory if I hadn't worshipped her.'

Dr Belgrave sipped tea and snuffled.

'Not to put too fine a point on it, I was Daisy's consolation for the last ten years of her life. She supervised my PhD. She talked me into Harvard. "Whatever I had she gave me again."'

There was no doubting the tears in Dr Belgrave's steely eyes.

'I remember her doing Founder's Day at school one year,' said Monica. 'She was amazingly thrilling.'

Dr Belgrave smiled gratitude.

'As you must have guessed by now,' she went on, 'Daisy left me her papers.'

Bognor was nearing a glorious end. He scraped chilly syrup off the sides of his glass as sleet slid down the window pane.

'With what object in view?'

Dr Belgrave chose to ignore this.

'I wanted to be a novelist,' she said, 'more than anything else. Daisy encouraged me, though I see now that she was misguided. I've burned them. You can't cross Barbara Pym with Henry Miller. At least I couldn't. They were embarrassing. It was Daisy who introduced me to Vernon. He was just starting out as a publisher. It seems a bloody long time ago.'

She rummaged in her satchel and pulled out a cigarette holder into which she screwed a Players Navy Cut *sans filtre*.

'Vernon said they were promising and that I was a "born writer". "Born bloody writer." The novels would come in good time, he said. Creativity couldn't be hurried. All that sort of crap. Meanwhile, he said, *The British Approach to Sex* would be a winner. I was broke, of course, and . . . oh, it was thirty years ago and the world was young and it seemed a good idea at the time and of course it made a small fortune. Made me a small fortune and Vernon, as ever, a rather larger one.'

She laughed and the smoke streamed from both nostrils, mingling with the steam from her black tea.

'You know how you get stuck in a relationship without ever quite realising that it's happened. It was true of me and Daisy and it was true of me and Vernon. Don't ask me to explain

90

about me and bloody Vernon because it defies logic. A marriage of warped minds, perhaps. Maybe I'm unnaturally susceptible to Svengalis. I don't know. It was a peculiar relationship but it was still a relationship.'

'Binding?' asked Monica.

'Oh, binding, yes, very.'

'What happened exactly?' Bognor tried to sound gently probing.

'After Daisy died I showed Vernon the papers. The diaries in particular.'

'Why?'

'I was distraught. I had to show them to someone. I know it may seem ridiculous but I trusted Vernon. He was my publisher. My friend.'

'Did you show them to him as a publisher or a friend?' Monica sounded ratty.

'I didn't discriminate in those days. It never occurred to me that he wasn't both.'

'And it was all there – Blunt, Philby, Burgess, Maclean? All the secrets spilled onto the pages of the diary?'

'Letters, too,' said Dr Belgrave. 'She'd kept copies of lots of her letters. It was almost as if . . . well, it's ridiculous but . . . '

'As if she'd meant the truth to be found out.'

'Yes.'

Dr Belgrave's cigarette had been lying untouched in the Pepsi-Cola ashtray. She tapped it out and lit another.

'Did you know any of this when she was alive?'

She frowned and the perplexity seemed genuine.

'I honestly don't know,' she said at last. 'I suppose I did. I mean she never made any secret of the fact that she knew all these upper-class nancies and she was obviously caught up in intelligence even though I could never quite work out how. But there was no grand confession.'

Bognor wanted tea. He waved at Mr Mozzarella and asked him for another cup and a fresh pot.

'So,' he said, 'you weren't entirely surprised by what was in the papers?'

'In general, no. In detail, yes. The Churchill story, for

instance. A lost weekend in Boulogne. That surprised me.'

'And Stalin?'

'I think that's Green jumping to conclusions. There was certainly a very drunken evening in a dacha but there's nothing to suggest she ever . . . the diaries are usually pretty explicit about that sort of thing.'

The tea arrived.

'I'm sorry,' said Bognor. 'I don't want to get too personal, but it may be important. You were shocked by what you found?'

Dr Belgrave considered this. She had a quite noticeable dark moustache.

'I'm not sure how to explain this,' she said. 'Yes, I was shocked, but not because there were a whole lot of revelations. It was just that I was suddenly confronted with something very private – the very private life of someone, well, of someone I loved. It made me realise how much there was of Daisy that I'd never really known. I thought I'd got beyond the façade but I hadn't. Not really. So, yes, it was pretty bloody. I'd assumed I was a true confidante but I wasn't. She'd used me just like she used everyone else.'

The Bognors turned away and looked out at the bleak midwinter while Dr Belgrave composed herself. It suddenly seemed almost as bleak in the Marine Ice Cream Parlour as the Bognors contemplated the wreckage of a life's love lost.

'You showed it to Vernon Hemlock as soon as you'd read it.'

'Yes. I needed to share it with someone.'

'You were already a successful Big Book author by then.'

'*The British Approach to Sex* had come out a year or so before. It sold a hundred thousand in hardback and there was a very lucrative paperback deal. And then the film rights.'

'*Orgasm!*' said Bognor.

'They were going to call it *Foreplay* at first but the Americans didn't like it. I remember they said they wanted something that delivered. Vernon dealt with all that side of things. I didn't want to get involved. It all seemed very tacky at the time. I was trying to do serious clinical work. The publicity got in the way. Has done ever since. I have to publish

92

my academic papers under an assumed name. Bloody absurd.'

Bognor's heart bled.

'And what was Hemlock's reaction?'

Dr Belgrave snorted.

'It was what you'd expect. "Dynamite" was the exact word. You've got to remember it was at least ten years before anyone knew about Blunt. It was only four years since Philby went to Moscow. Everybody thinks it's a good story now but it was a damn sight better story then.'

'So Hemlock wanted to publish?'

'Yes. He wanted me to edit the diaries myself and do them as diaries. He didn't want to use them as a basis for a biography or an exposé or anything else.'

'You persuaded him not to.'

Again Dr Belgrave had to think about this.

'Up to a point,' she said at last, but tentatively. 'He never stopped trying. But I was adamant. I was joint literary executor along with Saunders Horovitz, his literary agent, so I was in a position to veto it. Saunders was in favour, of course, because he wanted his ten per cent. Vernon never pushed too far, though. He may have thought me a bit of a goose but he knew I could lay a nestful of golden eggs. And even though Daisy's diaries would have been a sensation, they would have been a flash in the pan. No sequel. I had years ahead of me. My contract was so tight I couldn't have gone anywhere else but I could always have developed a terminal writer's block. Vernon didn't want that. He wanted a bloody Big Belgrave Book every third year at least.'

'I see.' Bognor pursed his lips. 'So let's bring ourselves up to date. How did Green get involved?'

Dr Belgrave sighed.

'I always had a soft spot for Vernon. Despite everything. I think there might even have been a time when I was a little in love with him. But you couldn't trust him. He didn't have it in him. Didn't know what it meant. Not his fault. Like being born without legs or having a cleft palate. It was a condition. Congenital. Couldn't be trusted. All that mattered to Vernon was Vernon.'

'But you did trust him?'

'At first. He made me a very rich woman. I was grateful. I thought it was more than just a commercial arrangement. That was what he told me.'

'When did he first show it to Green?'

'I don't know.'

'Did you let him keep the stuff?'

'No. That is, I lent it to him, for, oh, a couple of days. He must have made a copy.'

'Not what you intended?'

'I never thought about it.'

They stared at each other in silence. The naïvety in one so aggressively worldly-wise as Dr Belgrave was stunning. But it had been a long time ago.

'The idea of Green doing something on it only started to surface a year or so ago,' she said. 'Up until then Vernon had kept trying to persuade me to give him permission to do the diaries verbatim. Then he suddenly switched tack and started to go on about what a brilliant subject Daisy was for a biography. He even had the nerve to suggest a memoir. "My Life with Daisy". He had no idea of taste. That helped him in his business but hardly in private life.'

'Did Green approach you directly?'

'Not for a while. To start with it was just Vernon producing a series of innuendoes. Then we had lunch one day at the White Tower. I remember we'd been discussing the library and whether to include Lord Weymouth as a separate entry or just lump him into "Erotic murals". Then, suddenly, apropos of bugger all, he said, "By the way, Arthur Green's doing a real life story about your old girlfriend." That blew the bows off my sneakers, I can tell you.'

'What did you say?'

'I threw a wobbly. Left my dolmades untouched and walked out. We didn't speak for a month. Then he wrote me a long letter more or less apologising, but saying that Green had got the bit between his teeth and that he couldn't see how he could be stopped.'

'The papers were copyright?' said Bognor.

'Absolutely,' agreed Dr Belgrave, 'but the Green line was that he was using them merely as "the basis for research". If that was all he was doing then he was unstoppable.'

'Presumably you took legal advice?'

'Much good that did me. Long hours in chambers with learned counsel who did nothing but fudge and prevaricate while the money ticked up like a metronome. No, I'm afraid I took a very rat-like way out in the end. I went to the Intelligence services themselves. They knew about Daisy, it appeared. In fact they seemed to know everything about everybody, only they didn't do anything about it. I saw the top man. His main preoccupation was about "rocking the boat". "Whatever happens," I remember he kept saying, "we mustn't rock the boat." When I left he told me not to worry, he'd deal with it personally, have a word with Vernon, man to man. He was sure he'd see sense. He would appeal to his patriotism, bla, bla. In any case he thought they'd have him under the Official Secrets Act.'

'And that was it?'

'Yes,' said Dr Belgrave. 'He never mentioned it again. Not once. And I certainly wasn't going to.'

'Odd,' said Bognor, 'I was under the impression the security services didn't know anything about it until much more recently than that.'

Dr Belgrave gave him a very sharp look. Simultaneously Monica kicked him under the table.

'What makes you say that?' asked the Doctor.

'Oh,' said Bognor, flustered, 'just that no one told me.'

'No one ever does, darling,' said his wife, sweetly. 'After all, you're only Board of Trade.'

FIVE

Merlin Glatt was in the lounge bar of the Goose and Goblet, lurking behind the *Byfleet Bugle* and nursing a horse's neck. The room was empty and it seemed unlikely to Bognor that the *Bugle* would carry the cricket score from Australia. Nevertheless he asked.

'Rained off,' said Glatt, tersely. 'I don't want to risk being spotted here. There have been developments. My masters are not amused. Come to my room, number seventeen, in ten minutes' time. Knock three times.'

Monica and Simon glanced at each other with weary expressions of mild disbelief. Simon ordered two large Scotches and they sat down to wait.

'I suppose he really is one of us,' said Simon. 'Is his stuff really any good?'

'Yes,' said Monica. '"Loftus Road on the Night of the Newcastle Match" and "Hamster" are brilliant. "Box", of course, and "The Dartington Rhymes". I'm not sure about "South of the River Blues" or "Arts Council Bursary". But I'd say he was genuinely pretty good. All the experts say he's marvellous.'

'Well,' said Bognor grumpily, 'I'm not at all sure I trust him. Too arty-farty by half. He imitated Glatt's rather precious fogeyish voice: "Rained off . . . knock three times". I think he's been watching too much television. That's not the sort of stuff they teach you in "Tradecraft" at Hayling Island.'

'At least,' said Monica, 'we'd better play along with him. If he is a double agent we'll soon find out. I do agree the dual relationship with Romany Flange and Andover Strobe does give one pause for thought.'

They drained their glasses and went upstairs.

'Come,' said Glatt, as the third knock died away. When they entered he was adjusting his cravat in the glass.

'Several developments,' he said. 'Oh, do sit down, it'll have to be the bed for one of you. This isn't exactly the Ritz. I've taken the liberty of mixing Margaritas. I hope you'll join me. Good.'

He had even put salt round the rim of the glasses. Bognor frowned at it and at the poet with ever-deepening suspicion.

'*Salud!*' said Glatt, raising his glass.

'Cheers!' said Bognor.

Monica mumbled something non-committal.

'Well,' said Glatt, 'the first turn-up is that the scene-of-crime people discovered some yellow fibre between Audrey Hemlock's sheets. It matches the wool in Danvers Warrington's stockings.'

'Are you suggesting that Warrington and Audrey were having an affair?' asked Monica, licking salt.

'I don't know how else you can account for bits of his socks being in Audrey's bed,' said her husband. 'All the same, it's a bit of a so-what on its own. After all, Hemlock himself was given to knocking off all and sundry. A bit of tit-for-tat seems reasonable enough.'

Glatt gazed at him down his chiselled nose.

'Maybe,' he said, 'but coupled with the fact that Warrington seems to have gone off in rather a hurry it does seem odd.'

'Gone off in a hurry?'

'Yes. Capstick, too.'

Bognor crossed his legs. The bed on which he sat was old. The springs stuck into him and there was a deep valley in the middle which rendered his posture undignified as well as uncomfortable.

'What's the other turn-up?' he asked.

'I had a quick snoop round Hemlocks,' said Glatt, 'and found the butler had been keeping a diary. Explicit is hardly the word for it. It appears he'd been trying to blackmail Hemlock. What's more, he hadn't filled in the last couple of days, but the last entry for the day before Hemlock's death actually says . . .' Here Glatt referred to his own shorthand notes. '"Have given V. another twenty-four hours to come across. Situation dodgy. People are beginning to suspect. Hadn't realised what nasty minds writers had. I shall be glad to be shot of them all."'

Glatt looked up with satisfaction. 'Interesting, eh?' he said.

'Perhaps.' Bognor smiled, feeling that he might have the better of Glatt, particularly as the poet/agent had said that his real interest was in 'The First Woman' or 'First Lady'. He told Glatt about Green's presentation to the sales force and about the subsequent revelations from Dr Belgrave in Mr Mozzarella's ice cream parlour. At the end of it Merlin Glatt was like one of his Margaritas – visibly shaken.

'Hmmm,' he said, 'I have to confess we all missed that.'

'What?'

'The Belgrave connection. It explains a lot.'

'But not who killed the Hemlocks.'

'As I said to you earlier that's not my primary area of interest. You and Bumstead can feel free to fight that one out between you.' Glatt had got some composure back.

'Would Dr Belgrave have killed either Vernon or Audrey?' asked Monica.

Bognor shook his head. 'Only if she thought they were going to publish *The First Lady*. From what she said to us they were more or less happy not to. Vernon certainly. We don't know about Audrey.'

'Romany's obviously the one who's keenest,' said Glatt, 'God rot her.'

'Ideological reasons?' Bognor was genuinely curious.

'Greed,' said Glatt. 'Romany wouldn't understand ideology. As for Green, God knows. But I must say the Belgrave stuff is a revelation. Does she still have the original diaries?'

'I think so,' said Bognor. 'One thing bothers me, though. She says that she went to your people and spoke to the head man. Says she told him everything and that he shut up Hemlock.'

'She what?'

'Told all,' said Bognor. 'Years ago. Told your people.'

'Not possible,' said Glatt, 'I've seen the files. Nothing about Belgrave in them.'

'So she's lying?'

'Must be.' Glatt frowned.

'Why would she do that?' Bognor stared hard at the hunting print above the dressing table.

'Your guess is as good as mine,' said Glatt, without conviction. 'We'll have to take her in for questioning.'

'She'll say she made a full statement to your people years ago,' said Bognor, 'and you'll have a job proving she didn't.'

Glatt winced. 'That's my problem,' he said. 'Meanwhile, I suggest you have a word with Warrington about sex and Mrs Hemlock. Also enquire about the literary aspirations of the butler.'

The three of them toyed with their drinks. Bognor was all at sea.

'Glatt,' he said, gazing at the sensitive yet virile features of action man of letters, wondering to himself if there was real depth behind the Renaissance-man façade. He had a reputation for profundity, high seriousness, 'bottom', the sort of thing that distinguished the men from the boys. But was it merited? Was it real? 'Glatt, what's going on here? I mean, what do you think? Really?'

'My brief, as I told you, is to address the Byfleet Lit Soc tomorrow evening and prevent anyone – and I mean *anyone* – publishing the truth about Butskell-Godunov and her circle. As far as the murders are concerned, it seems to me most likely that Arthur Green and Romany Flange finally became exasperated by Hemlock's refusal to publish the 'First Lady' book and did him in. Then when Audrey said she would stick by Vernon's wishes they did her in, too. Tiresome of them. Particularly as we can't risk anything as public as a murder trial. All that Butskell-Godunov stuff spilling out under cross-examination from some nosey parker like Simpson QC would be even worse than publication. Still, with luck our friend Bumstead will manage to bark up the wrong tree and we'll get someone else convicted instead. Which will be much more satisfactory. Otherwise, we might have to stage a little accident ourselves.'

'Accident?' Bognor did not want to hear what he heard.

'Romany and her friend have become a serious nuisance,' said Glatt. 'If things don't take a speedy turn for the better they may well be involved in a fatal car crash. My people are rather expert at that kind of thing.'

Bognor swallowed hard.

'That's not on,' he said. 'You're employed by the Government. This is England.'

'Precisely,' said Glatt. 'If people like me weren't prepared to kill from time to time there'd be no such thing as democracy in this country. You can't faff about when it comes to an unpublished manuscript like this.'

Bognor swallowed again.

'I see,' he said.

A truculent smile played around the poet's thin cruel lips. 'I thought you would,' he said. ' " There must be many a pair of friends/who arm in arm, deserve the warm/moon-births and the long evening-ends." ' Then he laughed briefly. 'But no need for anything quite so drastic just yet,' he said. 'And now, if you'll excuse me, I have some reading to do. From now on I think it best if we stay away from each other. We'll adopt the old publisher's adage: "Don't call *me*, I'll call *you*." '

The Bognors let themselves out, traversed the lounge and stepped into the dank dark of Byfleet night.

'Brrr!' They shivered in unison, not so much from the cold as from the chill of their conversation.

'Was he serious?' asked Monica, putting an arm through her husband's.

'I thought so,' said Bognor. 'Not the least bit unserious. Gave me the impression of positively wanting to bump someone off.'

'And,' Monica shivered again, 'he's supposed to be having some sort of an affair with Romany Flange. Imagine killing your mistress.'

'Some people get a kick out of that sort of thing.'

'Meaning people like Glatt.'

'Meaning exactly that,' said Bognor. 'He's an obvious psychopath. A real pervert.'

'It does give an interesting extra dimension to some of the verse,' said Monica. 'You could interpret the "Dartington Rhymes" in a completely different way if you knew they were by the sort of man who could make snuff movies.'

'Is that so?' Bognor was not much interested in textual analysis of Glatt's poetry.

'Yes.' Monica squeezed his arm. 'Who'd have thought a gentle excursion into the world of publishing would have thrown up such a mess of death and intrigue?' she asked. 'I thought it was all about Bloomsbury and gentlemen in the Garrick and the Travellers and blue-stockinged Leavisites with PhDs in imagery in Smollett. I thought it would be fey and charming and literate. I thought it would be to do with fine writing and good books.'

'I knew it wasn't like that,' said Bognor, 'as soon as that little shit Prendergast went into publishing. Do you remember? – that spotty little Young Conservative in BNC who was sent down for flogging the typescript of the History Finals Papers.'

'Whatever happened to him?'

'He's managing director of one of the big paperback houses in the States. Par for the course.'

The streets of Byfleet were as gloomy as London's in the blitz. Those hoteliers who knew how to milk the tourists and trippers were soaking up sun in Barbados. The rest were, doubtless, cowering by twin-bar electric fires. The 'No Vacancy' signs were on display in front of the net curtains of practically every guest house in town; the shutters were shut at the Tropicana Fish Bar and Freddie's Freak Show and every single whelk, cockle, mussel and winkle stall. Even the street-lamps seemed to be on half power. A Big Book author would have described it as 'Stygian gloom'. Visibility zero, as near as dammit.

They had just ambled past a three-foot gap in the houses described as 'Blind Bo'sun's Alley' when Bognor suddenly felt something hard press into his back. As it did a female Bronx voice which seemed ludicrously out of place in this genteel English seaside town said: 'Just keep walking. Do as I say. Act natural. Any fancy Board of Trade heroics and you get led in one end and out the other.'

'We have company, Monica,' said Bognor, with a lightness he was far from feeling. 'Marlene Glopff, the aerobic queen and author of *Working Out with Glopff*, unless I'm much mistaken.'

There was a strong smell of distilled lilac. Not so much scent as something an athletic lady would splash on in the locker

101

room after a sauna and whirlpool. A hint of talc and sweat.

'Don't turn round; just do as I say. Walk.'

Mr and Mrs Bognor walked.

'I should have realised our American friends would become involved before long,' said Bognor, 'though I assumed they'd do things by the book. Official notification via Parkinson. That's the usual form.'

'Playing ball with the Brits,' said the Bronx voice, 'is like trying to play footsy with a faggot. Strike out every time.'

'Is she CIA?' asked Monica in her most Badminton Horse Trials voice.

'God alone knows,' said Bognor; 'amateur theatricals, I should say, but . . .'

The gun barrel, if that was what it was and Bognor was inclined to give it the benefit of the doubt, jabbed into him painfully.

'No chatter, please. Just do as you're told and you'll be all right.'

Bognor shut up and walked. He and Monica were still arm-in-arm and he squeezed back at her. It felt even colder than talking to Glatt.

Just ahead of them a 'C'-reg BMW saloon was parked, lights on, engine running.

'Mrs Bognor,' said Marlene, 'in the front. Mr Bognor in the back alongside *moi*. No funny stuff.'

'Absolutely not,' said Bognor, 'I'm much too intrigued.' He slid into the back seat and stared thoughtfully at the back of the driver's neck. The driver was wearing a chauffeur's cap but there was something familiar about his rear view.

'I say,' said Bognor, as the chauffeur gunned the car into action. 'Hastings!'

'Please don't talk to the driver,' said Marlene, 'he has to concentrate.'

Hastings was no mean motorist. He riffled through the gears like a saxophonist doing scales. Once out of town he allowed himself some gentle glides on icy bends. On the straights they touched the ton. Quite exhilarating.

'Well.' Bognor settled back into the seat and wished he were armed with the sort of Walther PPK that men like Glatt habitually carried. Or maybe not. He wouldn't have known what to do with it under circumstances like these. Talking his way out of trouble was the only way he knew. The gab was a better gift than gun as far as he was concerned. 'Are you going to tell me what's going on?'

Ms Glopff chuckled throatily.

'The reason we've taken you over, Mr Bognor, is that we want you to tell *us* what's going on.'

'We being you and the butler?'

She shoved at him with the gun barrel and he grunted with pain.

'I've been told you think you're a wise guy, Mr Bognor,' she said, 'but our records show that your boss Parkinson says you're not as funny as you think you are. So cut the comedy.'

He winced. 'Are you official?' he asked. Ms Glopff pulled out the ubiquitous laminated ID card. Bognor squinted at it. It could have been a driver's licence or a credit card for all he could tell but he nodded sagely at it all the same.

'You can put the gun away,' he said. 'I'm a paid-up subscriber to the Special Relationship. Anything I can do to help. Nothing too much trouble for Uncle Sam.'

'Treat everything with a pinch of salt, Marlene,' said Hastings, taking an 'S' bend with the aplomb of an Ayrton Senna. 'He may not be as funny as he thinks but he's not as stupid as he looks, either.'

'Thank you, Hastings,' said Bognor. 'Any time you want a reference . . . Anyway, how come you're working with the Americans?'

'I bet I know,' said Monica. 'Hastings is a mute inglorious Big Book author. For reasons we still don't know, Hemlock wouldn't publish him. Our friend here, however, has arranged through her employers to guarantee Hastings an American publisher for his novel. Or memoirs. Or whatever.'

'How did you know that?' Ms Glopff shifted her attention to the front seat.

'I guessed,' said Monica. 'It stands to reason. But I'd also like to know why Hastings stayed with Hemlock all those years.'

'Too many questions,' said Hastings, crashing the gears from four to two as they grappled with a sharp left hander. 'What have you told Merlin Glatt?'

'Who?' asked Bognor innocently.

Ms Glopff dug at him again with the gun.

'Cut that crap!' she said. 'I'm not stupid. We know who Glatt is. And we know he drove you into town and that you've just come from his room at the Goose.'

'Right,' said Bognor.

'And that you've been talking to another British agent, Molly Mortimer.'

'Molly's not a British agent,' said Bognor.

'She is so,' said Ms Glopff. 'Part-time but keen. And you talked to her after Green's presentation in the Winter Gardens.'

'Actually we were talking about the Royal Family. The Midgelys. Miranda Howard.'

Marlene Glopff obviously didn't believe this. She snorted.

'That schlock,' she said.

'No more than *Working Out with Glopff*,' said Bognor. 'In fact I should have thought you and the Midgelys could do an extremely lucrative combined effort. *Working Out with Royalty*. There's a *Big* Book if ever I heard of one.'

She jabbed him again with the gun barrel. 'I warned you once, buster,' she said. 'No jokes. No funny stuff.'

They were on the coast road heading south. An occasional shaft of thin moonlight caught the cliffs but it was still a murky night with scudding cloud and a misty drizzle. Hastings kept the windscreen wipers in overdrive. There was very little traffic. This part of the country gave every impression of having closed for the night. Halfway along a deserted straight they came on a signpost marked 'Reckitt Magna 3'. Hastings swung the car right and the hedgerows closed in on either side.

'Reckitt Magna,' said Monica; 'that's familiar.'

Bognor sensed her frowning in the front, willing herself to remember something from a footnote in the past.

'Got it,' she said. 'It's an early Glatt: "The Haven, Reckitt Magna". It's a writers' retreat like that place outside Reigate and the McDowell and the Yaddo in the States. Novelists go there to commune with each other and with nature, eat nut cutlets, beat their block. And all for under a pound a day.'

'Sounds like a CIA front,' said Bognor without thinking. He got another dig in the ribs for being unthinking out loud. Many a true word . . .

Ten minutes later the car passed through a sleeping hamlet, rattled left over a cattle grid and past a bungaloid lodge. The drive wound up through an avenue of beeches until debouching into a gravelled forecourt before a mansion of prep school dimensions and appearance. As they came to a crunching halt two large dogs emerged, barking.

Hastings lowered the window. 'Hodder, Stoughton, shut up, for God's sake! Major, get those bloody Airedales under control before I run them over!'

Bognor noticed a new Rolls Royce parked to one side of the porch. The number-plate was 'AS 1' and there was a 'disabled driver' sticker in the rear window.

Marlene Glopff alighted from the car with lissom grace as the Major reined in his hounds.

'Two more guests,' she said. 'Mr and Mrs Bognor. They can go in Coleridge.'

'They'll have to,' said the Major, 'it's the only double room left. Good evening, sir. Evening, madam. Welcome to the Haven.'

Mr and Mrs Bognor muttered.

'No luggage, Major,' said the butler. 'I'm afraid it's all been a bit sudden. But I dare say you can rustle a couple of toothbrushes up from stores. They'll only be with us the one night.'

Marlene Glopff led the way indoors.

'The Major will see you to your room,' she said, 'and you have five minutes to freshen up. Then we'll see you in the library.'

There was a gong in the hall; also a noticeboard covered with green felt. On it were pinned the times of the church and bus services as well as a note saying that cocoa was available at 25p, provided the housekeeper's office was told before teatime. The hall table was very shiny and smelt of beeswax.

105

'Upstairs, second on the left. The name's on the door. Bathroom's right opposite.' Marlene Glopff was almost self-consciously brisk. Now that she was apparently on home turf she had taken her right hand out of her coat pocket and Bognor was chilled to see that she was indeed armed. She held a small snub-nosed revolver which Bognor guessed was a Derringer. He wondered if it had a mother-of-pearl handle. 'And don't try anything clever,' she added; 'the drainpipe is not strong enough to support your weight, Hodder and Stoughton may not kill but they'll give you an awfully nasty bite, and we're miles from anywhere.'

The Bognors went upstairs in silence, aware of the triple gaze of Marlene, Hastings and the Major boring into their backs.

'Crikey!' said Bognor, closing the door of Coleridge behind them. 'What on earth is going on?'

The room was very plain. There were two iron bedsteads of institutional design and a gas fireplace with a reproduction oil painting of Samuel Coleridge-Taylor above it. The floors were polished wood, apart from two or three scattered and elderly rugs of vaguely Turcoman appearance. There was a wash basin in one corner.

Bognor went over to it and turned on both taps.

'Bound to be bugged,' he said. 'What *is* this place?'

'Like I said,' Monica said, 'it's a writers' retreat. Or was. Endowed by some old literary philanthropist in the thirties so that impecunious authors can get away from the enemies of promise – families, VAT men, society hostesses and all that. It used to be in south-west London somewhere but they sold it to a property developer a few years ago and moved out here. It's all coming back to me now. I think I must have read a piece about it somewhere like the *Literary Review*. I always thought it was perfectly legit. A bit loopy but harmless. I was obviously wrong. It's clearly been taken over by the CIA as a safe house.'

'What do you imagine they want?'

'Your guess is as good as mine,' said Monica, a touch frantically, 'but I suspect it's as the lady says. They're feeling left out by MI5 and 6 and they want to be let in on some secrets.'

'I think I should refer back to Parkinson. There must be some proper Anglo-American liaison at his level.'

'I wouldn't bank on it. Anyway it's too late for that. Are you having a pee?'

'Yes. After you.'

They peed in turn, both impressed by the Delft tiling in the loo as well as the heavy brass chain on the plug and the thick mahogany seat, both thinking hard about what to say and what to do next. It felt like a tight corner. And although Marlene and the Major claimed to be Official CIA they could just as well be from the Mob.

Downstairs they were surprised by the identity of their fellow guests. As they entered the library two other Big Book authors looked up: Milton Capstick and Danvers Warrington.

'Aha!' Bognor looked very hard at Danvers Warrington and wondered when to play the card of the vestigial piece of canary yellow stocking the forensic boys had found in Audrey Hemlock's bedroom.

'Enjoyed your talk last night, Capstick,' he said. Was it only last night? The Royal Institute of Letters seemed light years away, though the bruise on his head reminded him that it wasn't.

'Thank you very much, Bognor.' Capstick's polka dot bow tie bobbed with self importance. 'I'm sorry your view wasn't more widely shared. It's really rather pathetic to see how a certain sort of literary person makes poverty an art form. They seem to think making money from one's writing is a sign of philistinism. They've obviously never heard of Johnson. Johnson said there were few ways in which a man might be more innocently employed as in making money. That's not something you'll hear anyone endorse at the Royal Institute of Letters. Dear me, no!'

From outside, Bognor heard wheels trundling over polished boards. At first he thought it must be the Major or the housekeeper with a trolley of drinks but then he remembered the Rolls Royce with the disabled driver sticker and the 'AS 1' number plate.

Seconds later the wheelchair entered the library and he realised he was right.

Andover Strobe was driving the very latest thing in invalid carriages. Silky grey gunmetal with flashing lights. It looked like something designed by Lord Snowdon for Star Wars. He himself was wearing a magenta tracksuit and a gold cravat. The legs were short and enfeebled, the trunk and arms normal to large, the head enormous. He had low cheekbones, a less than generous mouth and opaque blue eyes. When he spoke it sounded like treacle processed in a cement mixer. He was smoking a Grade Lew cigar. Big. Expensive. A statement.

'Mr and Mrs Bognor, hi there. Welcome to the Haven. I'm Strobe. Take a pew. Great to have you aboard.'

The Bognors sat.

'OK,' said Strobe; 'publishing's a tough business and it's tougher still when you start tangling with issues of National Security.'

Bognor inclined his head but said nothing. Capstick and Warrington both smiled uneasily, Glopff and Hastings not at all.

'You're an intelligent man, I hear,' Strobe continued. He was unnaturally brown. Also bald. The great dome of his head shone like a seamless rugby ball. 'So you'll understand that I'm not about to let you or anyone else interfere with my plans now that they're reaching fruition.'

Bognor nodded again and maintained a superior-sounding silence. He could see that he was in for a lecture anyway.

'You will have discovered already', said Strobe, 'that Hemlock and I are the only two publishers in town. Everything else is mere dilettante rubbish. Gentlemen playing at trade, tradesmen pretending to be gentlemen. Give Hemlock his due – he was the only one who understood what in hell it was all about.' He waved the cigar expansively. 'Money, money, money and the power that money begets. Let's not faff around, Mr Bognor. Hemlock and I have never given a shit about "art" or "literature" let alone what some so-called publishers call "ethics". Do I make myself clear?'

'Absolutely,' said Bognor.

'There was a time,' and here Strobe's milky-blue eyes narrowed momentarily, 'there was a time when there was room

for the two of us but that time passed. There was a time –
maybe – when it was possible to be a seriously rich, seriously
powerful publisher based in London and controlled from
London. That time passed, too. People still talk about the
English language, God help them, but they're talking a lie. It's
been the American language and the American speaking
peoples since you were so high. You're smart and you know it,
but I tell you there are still arty farty little Englanders around
who think George III is on the throne.'

Strobe paused, examined the end of his cigar, frowned and
said, 'Major, will you find me a goddam light for this thing?'
and continued.

'You've heard of Megaword Universal?'

Again Bognor nodded. Biggest word shifters in the world –
hard-core pornography, do-it-yourself manuals, partworks,
videos, computer programs, even old-fashioned books. All
these and more were typeset and printed by sweated labour in
third-world countries, mainly in South East Asia, then beamed
via computerised satellite to Megaword's North American
headquarters on a private island in Cayuga Lake, upstate New
York. Megaword's pulp shunted around the seven seas under
every known flag of convenience. Megaword's slush funds and
ambiguously named deposits were in dodgy banks in Liechtenstein, the Cayman Islands, the Channel Islands and anywhere at
all where legitimacy was a dubious premise. Megaword was not
so much a publisher as a word broker employing every artifice
of the New Technology to get its words to every corner of the
globe. Megaword dealt with Moscow and Beijing and even had
a contract for Star War Manuals from the Pentagon. The
company made men like Strobe and Hemlock look like a couple
of down-and-outs dossing down in back numbers of the Daily
Maxwell under Hungerford Bridge. Not only that, it made them
look naïve and even honest by comparison.

Oddly, Megaword had never penetrated the British Isles.
The general impression was that the UK was too small to be
worth bothering with. Also too encumbered with Old Spanish
Customs – archaic, dilettante bosses and bothersome, union-
dominated employees. Much better concentrate your energies

on growth areas like South East Asia.

'As of Monday next,' said Strobe, leering round his cigar, 'I shall be President and Chief Operating Officer of Megaword Universal PLC (UK).'

'Congratulations,' said Bognor, 'though I rather doubt that will prove quite as cut and dried as you seem to think.'

'The arrangement is predicated on a number of assumptions guaranteed to be infrastructurally sound and meaningful,' said Strobe. 'I don't anticipate problems.'

'HMG won't like it,' said Bognor with a touch of rather prissy self-importance. 'The Government view is that British Publishing should stay British. It's like helicopters or . . . ah . . . er . . . Land Rovers. Part of the heritage. We at the Board of Trade take a very dim view of that sort of thing. Government are most unlikely to let it through.'

'Government, schgovernment,' said Mr Strobe. 'Megaword Universal is like what I said. Multi-national. The Megaword budget is bigger than most countries' and unlike most countries it makes a profit. If we set up a deal we set up a deal. Period.'

'And where exactly does that leave Big Books?' asked Bognor innocently.

'Like nowhere.' Strobe smiled. An unlovely sight. 'My friend Hemlock was negotiating with Megaword but he got greedy. Also we had Marlene on the team. Big help.' He leered at Ms Glopff who still held her pretty toy pistol. She looked disconcertingly fit and ruthless along with her over conventional all-American good looks. Like an early Bond girl or a Junior Joan Collins kewpie doll. 'And now we have Mr Capstick and Mr Warrington on our side, so the deal's all sewn up. Megaword were anxious that I should be able to deliver at least some of the Big Book authors. I hate to tell you this but the contract that these two gentlemen had negotiated with Big Books was just awful. They would have been in hock to Hemlock just as long as they lived.'

'Or *he* lived . . .'

There was no mistaking the scarcely camouflaged meaning between the line.

'Poor Hemlock,' said Strobe. And now he laughed. It was not

110

a very human sound – more like a lawnmower hitting stones. Bognor winced.

'Hemlock was murdered,' he said. 'In view of what you've just told me, your motive is stronger than anyone's.'

Again the lawnmower hit grit.

'Everyone but everyone wanted Vernon dead,' he said; 'matter of fact, I probably enjoyed him alive more than most. You need a sparring partner in life, and Vernon Hemlock was certainly that. Besides, I was nowhere near Hemlocks the night he died.'

'But your woman Glopff was. And your man Hastings. Not to mention Capstick and Warrington here.'

'Quite so,' said Strobe. 'So many suspects and yet, most unhappily, no fingerprints on the control that sent those two library shelves on their final fatal mission. Too sad. One of the great unsolved mysteries . . .'

This time Marlene and the butler joined in the laughter, though the two turncoat Big Book authors remained silent, shuffling their feet in embarrassment.

'What about *The First Lady*?' asked Bognor, shifting tack.

'What indeed?' said Strobe. 'I've heard too much about *The First Lady*. The matter's of no importance. What people like you would call a "red herring". Hemlock would never have published it. No more would I.'

'Megaword might, though,' said Bognor.

'I doubt that,' said Strobe. 'After all, the CIA does have a stake in the firm. Them and our Sicilian friends. So difficult, so often, to tell them apart I always think. Which parameters does Marlene come between, I ask myself. For which mob does she really work?'

'The CIA has an interest in discrediting British Intelligence,' said Bognor. 'It means they can pull rank whenever they want. Ignore us, patronise us, trample all over us, indulge in the world's most one-sided special relationship.'

'We do that already,' said Marlene, snickering. 'Mr Strobe's right. We'd like to see the manuscript. Ace item to hold over you Brits. But we have no interest in going public on it. Ivan's the only guy who has any non-commercial interest in seeing it published.'

111

'I'm not so sure,' said Bognor.

'Then get wise, Mr Bognor,' said Strobe. 'Be sure.'

Bognor shrugged. 'If you say so,' he said.

'I say so,' said Strobe. He placed the smouldering cigar in a chipped Groucho Club ashtray by his elbow and fished something that looked like a contract from the zip pocket on his tracksuit top. For a moment he studied it, lips puckered. Bognor noticed that they moved a little as he read – puckered or not.

'Right,' he said, when he'd done reading. 'To business. Delightful as this visit is, its purpose is not entirely social. To facilitate the finalisation of my current commercial undertakings, I need your signature on this.'

He handed the document to Bognor who read it, taking care to keep both lips stiff and immobile – a demonstration both of phlegm and of literacy.

It *was* a contract, and a detailed, punitive one at that. In effect it promised that the British Board of Trade would in no way interfere with the proposed takeover of Strobe's company by Megaword Universal nor would it prevent any British author who wished selling his services to the new company, notwithstanding any existing commercial arrangements. The real sting was in the preamble. This was a solemn undertaking that he Simon Bognor had fully investigated the affairs of both companies and given it as his considered opinion that there could be no sustainable objection to the newly proposed arrangement.

'I understand', said Strobe, 'that technically speaking you cannot speak for the Board. On the other hand it's going to be exceedingly difficult for the Board to overrule the findings of one of its most senior and experienced investigators. Particularly when he has been working on a paper on publishing these past few months. You're the expert, Bognor. Privately your superiors at the Board and in the Government may not give a toss what you say but if it's publicly known that you've given us the OK on the basis of your expert knowledge and privileged information then they have no alternative. "Government overrules its own report." Oh, I hardly think so.' He picked up the cigar and re-lit it, smiling all the time.

'I can't sign this,' said Bognor. 'More than my job's worth.'

'More than your life's worth if you don't,' said Strobe. 'I don't wish to seem unreasonable, Bognor, but you can see there's a lot at stake here. This deal is going through whether you like it or not. But if you do like it life will be a lot easier for me personally. I'll even guarantee that we publish a book of yours. Doesn't have to be your work on the Board of Trade. Could be anything at all. But if you don't sign I'm afraid you're going the way of Mr and Mrs Hemlock. A car accident tomorrow morning. A conflagration. Not wearing seat belts. Still drunk after the night before.' Mr Strobe made a show of examining the palms of his hands. 'You know the sort of thing,' he said.

'I need to think about it,' said Bognor. He was feeling chilly. 'How long do I have?'

Strobe consulted a heavy diver's watch which looked as near the state of the art as his wheelchair.

'You have till breakfast,' he said, 'which is always served at the civilised hour of nine o'clock. Choice of cereal, bacon and eggs, toast, tea or coffee. Isn't that right, Major? The Major has this place running like clockwork. Comes as a pleasant surprise to all the sloppy writing types who come here.' He paused and sighed. 'You're not going to sign now?'

Bognor shook his head. ''Fraid not,' he said. 'At least, I have to read the small print.'

'Pity,' said Strobe, 'I was hoping you'd join us for dinner, but as you've got so much to think about . . . well . . . there it is . . . the Major will show you back to your room. And please . . . no Scarlet Pimpernel heroics. There's electric fencing around the perimeter and Hodder and Stoughton are only the tip of the iceberg. There's a quartet of Dobermanns – Sidgwick and Jackson, Secker and Warburg – who'll do you a very nasty mischief given half a chance. And if they don't get you there's a bull-mastiff called Knopf who's only allowed out on very special occasions. I do assure you a nice neat car crash would be infinitely preferable.' Mr Strobe pressed a button on the arm of his chair and executed a neat 360-degree pirouette. 'If you do want a word before the night is through you'll find a bell push in your room. I shall be available at all times.' That laugh again, and a speedy departure as rubber tyres burned across the parquet.

The others followed him, leaving the Bognors with the Major. The Major coughed. Perhaps he was not used to being a gaoler. He seemed ill at ease, a small, put-upon person with a British soldier's version of a Hitler moustache, only ginger.

'Sorry about all this,' he said, 'but orders are orders. I can send up beer and sandwiches if you'd like. Or cocoa. The Haven's famous for its cocoa. Our own cows and we always make it with proper chocolate – Bournville plain – none of your synthetic muck!'

'That would be very nice, Major,' said Monica, dimpling. 'Thank you so much. We'll make our own way back, thank you.'

'Corned beef? Spam? Cheese and chutney?' he chuntered, standing in the doorway, only carrying out orders. 'Beer or cocoa?'

'A selection, I think, Major,' said Monica. She was at her most serene under threat and the way she swept up the stairs was magnificent, causing the Major to catch his breath and acknowledge that there went a remarkably fine woman, of the sort that had become sadly scarce in modern Britain.

Back in their room some of the Force Five went out of Monica's spinnaker.

'What are you going to do?' she asked, leaning against the door, deflating before her husband's very eyes.

'No point trying to escape,' he said.

'None.'

'That's settled, then.' He went to the window and looked out. A luminous cordon encircled the house under the pretext, he supposed, of illuminating the historic exterior for the benefit of aesthetes, authors and others. He guessed there would be other lights ready to snap on as soon as the alarm was triggered. Somewhere out in the park a dog howled, a low, back-of-the-throat moan, guaranteed to turn blood to vermilion sorbet.

114

Hodder, Sidgwick or even Knopf. An owl hooted, followed a second later by an answering call, soft and sinister in the velvet night.

'I could just sign it,' he said, turning back to face Monica.

'Parkinson would never forgive you.' She had kicked her shoes off and was lying on the bed, hands clasped behind her head, staring at the ceiling. 'End of your career.'

'Better than the end of one's life in some CIA-rigged car crash, doused in whisky and kerosene. Even after one of the Major's breakfasts.'

'True,' Monica mused, 'and I suppose you could always say it was signed under duress. That Andover Strobe threatened to pull your fingernails out.'

'No one's likely to believe that.'

'No.'

'But if I don't sign it,' Bognor caressed the edge of a rug with the toe of his brogues, 'we won't live to see tomorrow morning's tea break.'

'No option,' said Monica, 'so the question becomes essentially gastronomic. Do you sign at once and have a decent dinner with Mr Strobe and friends or do we wait until tomorrow, in which case we dine on Spam sandwiches and pale ale?'

'Socio-gastronomic rather than just gastronomic,' said Bognor; 'I'm sure the food would be better chez Strobe, but the company here is infinitely preferable.'

'Darling,' smiled Mrs Bognor, 'still gallant after all these years.'

'Not gallant at all,' said her husband. 'Merely the truth.' He was still, after all these years, embarrassed and uneasy when it came to compliments. Not at home with the romantic gesture, even at home. He would like to have been a male chauvinist pig but he did not have it in him.

There was a knock at the door.

'Sandwiches,' he said, walking across and opening it.

Room service turned out to be provided by Danvers Warrington.

'Aha!' he exclaimed in a stage hiss, 'I persuaded the Major to part with a perfectly decent claret – the Château Magnol 'eighty-one. Only a Cru Bourgeois but an Haut-Médoc. I think you'll be amused by it. I can't say the same for the sandwiches.'

'They look like pretty serious sandwiches,' said Monica, eyeing the curl of the crust with blunt anticipation.

'Deadly,' said Danvers. 'You simply can't make a decent sandwich without a *crème raifort* or a *beurre printanier*. The Major's imagination when it comes to such matters barely extends to the *moutarde*. If you'd like something afterwards I dare say I could rustle up some port. I've had my eye on a bottle of the Fonseca 'sixty-six which has somehow strayed into the cellar. You'd be more than amused by that.' He closed his eyes and recited: '"Very fine, slightly spicy, classic bouquet; sweet, full, soft, lovely wine, fruity with good grip at the finish. Magnificent."'

Bognor lifted the corner of a corned beef sandwich and replaced it.

'The forensic boys', he said, 'found some yellow wool in Audrey Hemlock's bedroom. What do you make of that?'

Danvers Warrington's monocle slipped from his eye and the tray almost slipped from his grasp.

'Yellow wool,' he repeated, putting the tray down on the glass top of the Maples dressing table. 'In Audrey Hemlock's bedroom.'

'Yellow wool which exactly matched the wool in your own canary yellow stockings, Warrington.' Bognor poured three glasses of the Cru Bourgeois from the Haut-Médoc.

'Wool, Warrington,' he said, handing round the glasses. 'I think it proves that you were in Audrey's room the night Vernon was murdered.'

Warrington slurped his wine with less attention than one would have expected from one of his less conscientious readers.

'I wanted to talk to you about Audrey,' he said, 'about Audrey and *moi*.'

'That's a happy coincidence,' said Bognor, 'because I was going to ask you about just that.'

'It's true,' said Warrington, 'Audrey and I did have a bit of a thing going on. I think I told you what a swine Hemlock was.'

'You did.' The Château Magnol was certainly more amusing

116

than the sandwiches. Bognor sipped it appreciatively and tried
to think of some good winebore words to describe it.

'He was a swine to his authors, a swine to his staff, a swine to
his competitors, but above all he was a swine to his wife.'

'At least he didn't kill her.'

'That's a singularly ungracious remark.'

'True, nonetheless. Someone killed Audrey and the one
person it can't have been is nasty old Vernon. You on the other
hand, as Audrey's lover, might . . . I mean, *crime passionnel*
and all that.'

'That's ridiculous . . . *une idée folle*.' Warrington blew on his
monocle and polished it with his snuffly red kerchief. 'However,
I do concede that I had a double motive for doing away with
Hemlock himself. First as an exploited author and second as his
wife's lover.'

'It's all very well saying you were exploited,' said Bognor
with the venom peculiar to a poorly salaried, much-maligned
civil servant, 'but the fact of the matter is that you're a damn
sight richer than most of us and if it hadn't been for Hemlock
publishing your plonk books you'd be back in the rut with
everyone else.'

'I'd have been a lot better off with Strobe. Once Megaword
are in charge I'll be really well off. We all will.'

'Those of you who take the Yankee dollar,' said Monica.
Monica could be patriotic in the tartest memsahib manner when
the mood took her. Something to do with Daddy, the Brigadier.

'That sounds like greed,' said Bognor. 'Greed sounds like a
motive. For murder, maybe.'

'It's very far from greed, *mon brave*,' said Warrington,
aggrieved. 'I just want an honest day's wage for an honest day's
work.'

'I seem to remember you saying "pish tush" not so long ago.
Well, "pish, tush" to you too. I think you killed Vernon
Hemlock because you wanted his wife all to yourself. And I
think you thought that she'd take over the business and pay you
whatever advance or royalty you wanted.'

'I couldn't have killed Vernon.'

'Why not?'

'Because I was with Audrey.'

'In bed with Audrey.'

'Since you mention it, yes. In bed with Audrey.'

'She'd have vouched for you, I suppose?' Bognor half wondered why he was being so aggressive with Warrington. Was it his success that he resented, or his pretensions? Or did he really think he was a murderer?

Warrington glowered.

'Simon doesn't mean to be insensitive,' said Monica; 'he has a job to do, and it's not easy. Frankly it seems to be getting more difficult every minute. Why did you want to tell us about your liaison with poor Audrey?'

'Because I wanted to make you realise that I was as keen to discover her murderer as you are. Make you understand that I'm on your side. Not like the others.'

Bognor let this pass with a raised eyebrow, but latched on to the first sentence instead.

'What makes you think she was murdered? The official line is that she killed herself. Overdose.'

'Poppycock,' said Warrington. 'The only person who believes – or affects to believe – that she committed suicide is that ass Bumstead. I more than anyone know that Audrey would never have done such a thing. Especially not . . . especially not under the circumstances.'

'You mean especially not with the appalling Vernon out of the way.'

Warrington swilled and sniffed and held his glass to the light.

'I suppose', he said lamely, 'that I do mean that.'

'Although,' said Monica, 'she was terribly upset by Vernon's death. I know. I had to comfort her.'

'Shock,' said Warrington. 'Guilt. Hemlock's death was the beginning of a new life.' He dabbed under his monocle and there was a catch in his voice. 'A new life for both of us. Suicide's unthinkable.'

Bognor thought Danvers Warrington an unspeakable old ham but he was also inclined to think he had a point. He refilled their glasses and they all stared into them. Outside, the owl hooted again and the dogs barked. A door opened and they

'Surely some mistake?' said Bognor, when they had left.

Bumstead glowered. 'Any mistakes in this case have been the result of outside interference and of my paying attention to amateurs.'

'I see,' said Bognor. 'So now you've got it all sewn up?'

'It doesn't help,' said Bumstead, 'when people like you come muscling in on my patch and then get yourselves kidnapped. It doesn't help at all.'

'I do see that,' said Bognor. 'On the other hand one doesn't expect to have American keep-fit ladies ambushing one in the main street of English seaside resorts. Especially out of season. And at least we led you here.'

'Up to a point,' said Glatt, 'but as I told you, the Major is one of ours. We knew what was up. We were going to stage a dawn raid but after consulting with your Mr Parkinson at BOT HQ we agreed to come early in case anything happened to you. Mr Parkinson was quite adamant and I'm sorry to say he pulled rank. Personally I'd have waited.'

'Me too,' said Bumstead.

'Your man Parkinson wants a word, by the way,' added Glatt. 'We've sealed off Hemlocks so you've got a room in the Goose and Goblet annexe. Tomorrow morning it's back to London, p.d.q. We're all agreed on that. Nothing more for you to do down here.'

'Except get in the way.' Bumstead smiled at Glatt. It was the smile of a would-be conspirator. Equal to equal.

Glatt did not respond.

SIX

Parkinson was his usual lugubrious, unamused self.

'A crippled publisher in a magenta tracksuit, eh?' he said; 'made his getaway in a helicopter, whereupon a poet in a black leotard came swinging in from a nearby monkey puzzle tree crying out "Me Byron! You Bognor!"'

'You're exaggerating,' said Bognor.

'I'm exaggerating, laddie,' Parkinson's voice could have corroded copper, 'I'm exaggerating. Baron Munchausen to you too. Listen, Bognor, this was a routine low-key exercise. You were required to produce a Mauve Paper on the Publishing Industry, not a Yellow Book. You are a Board of Trade minion, a penpusher, a low form of life. Yet you come to me with a tale of two murders. You tell me you have been hit on the head outside the Russian Embassy, that one of our bestseller writers is about to blow the gaffe on the sainted memory of Daisy Butskell-Godunov, casting aspersions on half White's, Trinity and the Brigade or Guards at the same time, and now you give me a space-age wheelchair which whisks this limbless pornographer into a CIA helicopter and off to the flight deck of the USS *Brontosaurus* from which doubtless to the very Oval Office itself. "Aw, shucks, Bognor." Isn't that what the President of the United States will say next time you bump into him? Dear God, what have I done to deserve you?'

'There's no need to be like that,' said Bognor, none too amused himself.

'I've had that tiresome little man, your old friend Weinstube, trying to wheedle his way past the secretaries every hour of the day and night. He appears to think that a junior minister is entitled to do that. A very junior minister indeed. But I have to tell you, Bognor, that I have had senior ministers on the telephone to me about this one. Very senior ministers indeed. Not to mention the Cabinet Secretary herself. The Dame is not amused. Nor am I. I want you back in the office a.s.a.p. Then I shall have you chained to your desk and deprived of the telephone. There are mountains of correspondence relating to petty fraud in the postal service. That should keep you gainfully employed until you take early retirement.'

'But there are murders to be solved,' protested Parkinson's Special Investigator. 'A Mauve Paper to get out. A book to write. Work to be done.'

'Not by you, sunshine.' Bognor's boss was at his most adamant. 'Your time is finally up. I want you back here under lock and key. There are quite enough people involved already. We appear to have the police *and* the security authorities all charging around the countryside attempting to solve crimes. It's my view and the minister's view that this is no longer a Board of Trade matter. My purpose in life has long been to ensure that this Department has gravitas and what the political commentators like to call "bottom". It has to be said, Bognor, that on present form you seem to have neither gravitas nor bottom. It is painful for me to have to say these things but I will not shrink from the truth.'

'I do see that,' said Bognor, 'but I've been with this thing since the beginning and I want to see it through.'

'No.'

'Just one more day.'

'I said *no*.'

'Not even a few more hours?'

'You are trying my patience, Bognor.'

'Then just tell me one thing – is Glatt one of ours?'

'Just what precisely do you mean by that curious phrase?'

'Exactly that,' said Bognor. 'I mean is he playing for us or the opposition?'

'These are grey areas,' said Parkinson. Bognor thought he discerned a marginally less adamantine tone. Parkinson's voice had, as it were, softened from diamond to flint. 'The good book tells us that he that is not for us is against us. It's a useful maxim for life, Bognor. You'd do well to heed it.'

'He doesn't work for the Americans?'

'My information', said Parkinson, picking words with the

125

careful fastidiousness of a hiker crossing a stream on stepping stones, 'is that he is on the books of Five.'

'Is that good information?'

'This is an open line, Bognor.'

'I'm aware of that, but I need to know.'

'Let me put it this way,' said Parkinson, still picking his way through the language with care. 'Five think he works for Five. I have other information which suggests – only suggests, mark you – that Six believe him to be working for them.'

'I see.' Bognor did not see clearly but a shape was beginning to emerge.

'Are . . . I mean . . . would I be altogether wrong in thinking that Five and Six are, as it were, at sixes and sevens?'

There was a long, choleric pause. Eventually Parkinson, his voice shaking with an emotion at which Bognor could only wildly surmise, said, 'I want you back in the office by lunchtime or I'll tell that Bumstead creature to clap you in irons and have you frog-marched here.'

A dull click and he was gone.

Bognor swore, several times, quite loudly.

Monica smiled sympathy. 'Parkinson in one of his moods, darling?'

'He thought I was trying to be funny. Why on earth can't I get him to take me seriously? Nobody bloody well takes me seriously.'

Monica demurred. 'I take you quite seriously. Often.'

'That's not what I mean.'

'Thank you.'

'Oh, I'm sorry.' Bognor ran a hand through thinning hair and shook his head as if trying to dislodge something alien that had got stuck in it. 'I didn't mean it like that. It's just that . . . well, you know what I mean.'

'Yes.'

She did, too.

'I feel, you see,' he said, groping somewhat, 'that we're within an ace of solving this one. But I do wish it were more like a classic Hemlock Big Book. You know. Good Guys, Bad Guys, never the twain shall meet. Also, beginning, middle and end. There are too many ambiguities here and broken conventions. The Americans, for instance. They're supposed to be on our side.'

'So they are,' said Monica, 'with the exception of Marlene Glopff.'

'But even Marlene Glopff', said Bognor, 'may think she's on our side.'

'She has a funny way of showing it. Sticking her itty bitty little gun in your ribs. With friends like that who needs enemies?'

'She may be serving a Greater Truth.'

Monica smiled. 'She may *think* she's serving a greater truth. Do you think she killed Hemlock?'

'Somehow I doubt it,' said Bognor. 'It seems to me that no matter how tight Hemlock's contracts may have been they could always be got out of. If Glopff's aim was to get control of British publishing for the Americans she could have done it without killing Hemlock. With Megaword money Andover Strobe could have made any Big Book author an offer he couldn't refuse and that even Hemlock couldn't match.'

'I wonder if they've found Strobe and the others.'

'The helicopter range can't be that great. On the other hand he's bound to have getaway cars.'

'Bit silly, shooting the lights out like that.' Monica shivered at the memory. 'Guns and things. Terribly unBritish. An admission of guilt, too. He's had it now – long-term.'

'That was the Major. Carrying out orders.'

'I thought the Major was one of ours after all?'

'Yes, but he couldn't let Strobe know that. If he hadn't shot out the lights, Strobe would have guessed.'

'I suppose so.'

It was late. One in the morning. They were tired. The annexe of the Goose and Goblet was draughty and spartan but the bed was sprung and the sheets were clean. The Bognors undressed and washed, got into the bed, turned out the lights, but could not sleep.

'The Midgelys, Ann Belgrave, Capstick, Warrington, Arthur Green, Romany Flange,' said Monica.

'And Hastings,' said Bognor, 'if you're running through suspects.'

'And Hastings. Funny sort of butler.'

'Yes.'

Bognor turned over, sat up, plumped his pillow, lay on his back.

'The fact,' he said, 'that both Warrington and Capstick have defected to Strobe within forty-eight hours of Hemlock's death certainly strengthens their motive.'

'Warrington wouldn't have defected if Audrey were still alive.'

'True. But if he was going to become Mr Audrey in succession to Hemlock that surely makes the motive even stronger.'

Monica giggled. 'You think he killed for Audrey?'

'That and the prospect of becoming boss of Big Books PLC.'

'It's a theory.'

'I can't see that the Midgelys are seriously in the murder stakes. They did very well out of Hemlock. Much better off having him alive. I'm ruling them out. The books are completely worthless. It's only Hemlock's hype that made them sell.'

'Maybe Strobe could have hyped them better.'

'Hmmmm. Up to a point.'

They were silent for a while. Monica began to snore very lightly.

'Of course,' said Bognor, 'Arthur Green and Romany Flange are the most suspicious of the lot. Do you imagine there's anything sexual going on there?'

'Oh, do put a sock in it, Simon, I'm trying to sleep. Romany Flange was already knocking off Hemlock and Glatt. Surely that's enough in these days of the universal French letter?'

'Romany Flange looks insatiable to me.' He turned on his side. 'And if Vernon Hemlock absolutely refused to publish *The First Lady* then killing him might have seemed the only way out.'

'I don't believe authors kill their publishers for refusing their books,' said Monica. 'They merely take them elsewhere. Now if you're going to get back to the office in time for lunch you'd better get some sleep.

'On the other hand,' said Bognor, 'isn't it just as likely that Dr Belgrave would have killed him if he had decided he *was* going to publish *The First Lady*?'

'But he didn't, so she didn't either, now please go to sleep.'

'Could be bluff.'

Monica put her head under one of her pillows and ground her teeth.

'The trouble is: no dabs. Not a fingerprint anywhere on the wheel that controlled the "S" shelves. There just isn't going to be any convincing forensic evidence. So we have to give the murderer . . . or the murderer*s* . . . enough rope. It's going to mean a stroke of luck or some devilish questioning. Maybe both.'

He turned over onto his stomach again.

'Perhaps it is all down to Strobe and the CIA,' he said. 'The logic is unassailable. Strobe and Megaword want control of Big Books. Hemlock won't budge so they kill him. Then Audrey won't budge either so they kill her too. Strobe wasn't in the house and anyway he'd find it difficult managing the stairs even in that fancy wheelchair. So he'd infiltrated Marlene Glopff – or rather the CIA had – and she or someone else had suborned the butler. So one of them dunnit . . .'

Monica began to weep softly so he talked more quietly to himself, tailing away into a whisper, then into an internal monologue and finally sleep. Not that he found respite there, for he dreamed extraordinary dreams of Bigger and Bigger Books, books in which even the words grew and grew until they became so enormous that they were too big to read, too big even to get on the page so that page after page was pure blank white with nothing on it but a terrible creeping red stain which spread and spread until every page of every book was damp and sticky with fresh spilt blood and then the microphone started to whine louder and louder and louder and louder with the voice of the fierce woman from the RIL mixing with the whinge of DCI Bumstead and the crisp telephonic retribution of Parkinson and the schmaltzy nothingness of Cynthia Midgely and the threatening Bronx of Marlene Glopff with her rippling pectorals and uncomfortable little gun and the waves beat against the jetty and the fairy lights rattled in the wind and . . . '*Oh my God wassamatta! Help. What time is it?*'

'God! You were snoring! I couldn't do anything with you. Great mouth wide open and lying flat on your back and the whole room trembling. It's after seven.' Monica was standing at the foot of the bed frothing at the mouth. She had a toothbrush in one hand and most of the bedclothes in the other.

'You've stripped the bed,' said Bognor.

'I couldn't stand the noise,' she said, dropping the blankets and fizzing the brush across her gums. 'I shall be glad to get out of Byfleet. I don't think it's my sort of place.'

'I was having a dream,' he said, rubbing his eyes. 'Gosh, I slept badly.'

'Rubbish!' Monica rinsed her mouth with water from a plastic mug. 'I was the one who slept badly. Every time I nodded off I was woken by your snoring. I wonder who's dead this morning.'

'What do you mean?'

'First it was Mr Hemlock. Then it was Mrs Hemlock. You know these things go in threes.'

'I can't bear it when you're superstitious.'

'I'm not being superstitious. It's a well known fact.'

'I think we've had enough corpses for one case. I hardly ever have more than two per case. You know that.'

'You don't usually have a trigger-happy Jane Fonda lookalike rampaging around the country in a helicopter, nor a double-agent major with a rifle, let alone an entire regional anti-terrorist squad. This case is bigger than your usual.'

'It does seem to have escalated.' Bognor swung his legs onto the floor. 'Nevertheless I think this is where the killing has to stop. Too many authors behaving like the characters they create.'

'The publishers are behaving worse than the authors.'

'Up to a point.' He yawned and pulled a palm across stubbly jowls. 'The authors haven't lost any of their people yet. The publishers have two dead already.'

'You're implying they were killed by the authors. Civil war in the book industry?' She glanced at his feet. 'Oh, Simon, you are revolting. Did you sleep in your socks?'

'I was cold.' He ambled to the washbasin and squeezed toothpaste onto his brush. 'Extraordinary dreams,' he said, 'all about blood and books.'

'Don't tell before breakfast,' said Monica, pulling on tights, 'otherwise they'll come true.'

Bognor spat. 'Now that *is* superstitious. In the dream all the books I was looking at had completely blank pages which were covered in blood. And I defy you to demonstrate how that can possibly become true. I wonder if the Goose and Goblet does a proper cooked breakfast. I am absolutely not eating any muesli.'

Monica sighed. It was part dismay and part agreement. So much about her husband was disastrous and yet, on the whole, it was the disastrous parts that she was so fond of. She knew that he ought to sleep with his socks off and that he shouldn't have fried egg, bacon, sausage, tomatoes and bread for breakfast. And yet if he had been a muesli man she would never have married him.

It was a fine crisp morning after the dank drizzle of the night. Bognor hummed a little as he crossed Anchor Street to the newsagent's where he bought a *Globe*. In the dining room he sprinkled demerara on his cornflakes, smiled at Monica and only then turned to the paper. Molly Mortimer had made the front page:

> HEMLOCK WIDOW FOUND DEAD
> MYSTERY OF GREEN FACTOID
> PLOT THICKENS
> By Molly Mortimer, Literary Editor.

Not often the Literary Editor strayed outside the Thursday books page or the sombre euphemisms of the obituary columns. Bognor read with mild amusement. Molly's piece suggested more than it revealed – more smoke than fire. She had obviously got an inkling of the Flange–Green axis and she knew there was a *Big* Big Book in the wind. She had also guessed (or been told, but Bognor's intuition suggested the former) that it was a break into non-fiction. To his horror he also read that 'Britain's book business, notorious for its long lunches and amateurism, has recently been attracting the attention of the Board of Trade. The BOT is keen to put more muscle into the export of British words and one of the Board's most senior civil servants is in Byfleet-next-the-Sea where he has been conducting lengthy investigations into Big Books PLC. The investigator, Mr Simon Bognor, 43, was unavailable for comment late last night, but Whitehall sources did not rule out the possibility of powerful American interest in the stricken British publishing house. Among British competitors waiting to pounce on the ailing giant, the name of Mr Andover Strobe, the 54-year-old crippled book broker is most often mentioned. It is believed that there would be stern resistance in Government circles to an American takeover. Former Tory Party Deputy Chairman Jeffrey . . .' Bognor put the paper down and took a mouthful of cereal. He did not want political effusions at breakfast. He wondered what Molly had written originally. The article had all the hallmarks of what a certain sort of sub called 'creative editing'. It meant that Bromley man (all sub-editors in his experience lived in semi-detached houses in Bromley) had taken Molly's original and turned it into Globespeak, altering everything including 'facts' to accord with his own Bromley semi-detached view of life.

The Goose and Goblet dining room was peopled by solitary commercial travellers all sitting at separate tables, all munching disconsolately and staring at anything they could find to stare at except for each other. Usually tablecloth or ceiling.

Into this sad, silent mastication a moment later there erupted the lady of the press, cloaked though undaggered, striding in with the haggard yet superior expression of one who has been up all night.

'Darlings!' she said, seeing the Bognors, 'thank heaven I've found you.'

Commercial travellers' eyes swivelled towards her like extra-terrestrial antennae. She was not what one associated with Byfleet-next-the-Sea, even in high season, even at the end of the pier show.

She came and sat down at their table, quelled the travellers with a raking stare, and demanded coffee from their clumping wide-eyed waitress.

'Bloody good story!' she said, in a husky whisper. She leaned towards Bognor and winked. 'I don't know how you do it.' She turned to Monica. 'I adore your husband,' she said. 'He's such a dark horse. Wherever he goes people start dropping dead in the most delicious circumstances. I don't know how he does it.' She reverted to Bognor himself. 'The News Desk rang in the middle of the night with some stuff about shooty-bangs at a writers' retreat. And my sources say that the local constabulary have taken in Milton Capstick and Danvers Warrington for questioning. And a helicopter has been found abandoned at the old RAF base at Norton Fitzpriors and Hemlock's butler has gone AWOL. Now what can you tell me?'

'No comment.'

'Oh, sugar puff.'

'Molly, it's more than my life's worth. Honestly.'

'I'll trade you.'

'Trade me what?'

'Information. Good stuff. Useful.' The coffee arrived – the thin sour stuff you still get in English towns.

'But Molly, even if I was interested in whatever it is that you're offering I don't think I have anything to give in exchange.'

'A little bird told me you were involved in the shooty-bangs. Small village, name of Reckitt Magna.' She drank some coffee, pulled a face and took a long, thin cheroot from her shoulder bag.

'I could use a large brandy,' she said; 'bloody British licensing laws.'

'Who told you I was at Reckitt Magna?'

'Darling, I don't reveal sources, but you ought to know by now that the *Globe* has informants everywhere. Distressed gentlefolk in reduced circumstances; retired military personnel on fixed pensions; the vast army of the unemployed; any-one with a score to settle. They all get on the blower to

Aunty Molly and her friends the second anything stirs in the woodshed.'

Bognor was well into his egg and bacon. He wondered if the Major's breakfast would have been better. This was a touch greasy and the grease was a touch rancid.

'You want to know what happened at Reckitt Magna.'

'Please!' Molly made a kissing face. She had smudged on some lurid lipstick which overlapped her lips.

'I'll see you,' said Bognor, 'but I'd like some circumspection. I didn't much care for this morning's stuff. I'm supposed to be incognito. And who told you I was forty-three?'

'Isn't he enchanting?' Molly asked Monica. Monica was looking frosty and not disposed to enter into the discussion.

'I met one of the local fisherfolk last night,' said Molly, 'in a dive by the harbour called the Mermaid's Tail. We got talking.' She swilled coffee and stifled the taste with smoke. 'He was quite good on the local gossip, especially after a few shots of Pernod and black.'

'You what?' said Bognor, shocked.

'Pernod and blackcurrant,' said Molly. 'It's what the young drink. He was a juvenile fisherman. Quite dishy if you like touselled beefcake with tattoos.'

'Not my style,' said Bognor. 'But do go on.'

'He said someone had chartered his boat for a fishing trip.'

Bognor waited. The bacon rind was hairy. He cut it off and chewed the meat.

'Yes . . .' he said.

'Well, don't you think that's peculiar?'

'He's a fisherman,' said Bognor. 'Presumably he has a fishing boat. It's presumably for hire. It all seems quite normal to me.'

'In the dead of winter?'

'No accounting for taste. This is England. Mad dogs and all that.'

Bognor was irritated. Molly was trying to tell him something but for a journalist she was being maddeningly elliptical. Normally she would take a rumour and elevate it into the truth. Now she was doing the reverse.

'Two people, as a matter of fact,' she said, 'booked in the name of Smith. Mr and Mrs.'

'What are you trying to tell me?'

'I'm not trying to tell you anything. Just telling you. My fisherman said that a rather sexy, well-turned-out woman who didn't look in the least like a fishing person booked his boat for a couple of hours tomorrow morning. And given all the peculiar events taking place in the wake of the Big Books sales conference I think that's a pretty suspicious fact.'

'You do?'

'I do.'

'Who do you think it is? – assuming it's not a Mr and Mrs Smith.'

'Your guess is as good as mine but my fisherman was quite smitten. And he emphasised the turn-out.'

'American?'

'No, it's not the glamorous Glopff.'

'Romany Flange.'

'That's what I thought.'

Bognor contemplated the marmalade. It was ersatz Oxford.

'And she booked for two?'

Molly breathed smoke through flared nostrils. She looked like a thoroughbred newly out to grass.

'For two. Yes.'

Bognor glanced at his wife. 'Arthur Green equals Mr Smith?'

'My hunch is the same as your hunch.'

'But why?'

'What time?'

'He said half-past ten,' said Molly through eyes half closed with fatigue and conspiracy.

It was just after eight.

'I'm supposed to be in the office before lunch.' Crisis always made Bognor greedy. He succumbed to the temptation of the marmalade. If ever he won the pools he would take a week at a health farm.

'What do you think, darling?' he asked his wife.

'I think you should get back to the office before lunch. If the connection at Bradleigh Parkway actually connects that means the nine-ten.'

135

'You really think that?'

'It's your job. Your future. Your problem. You just asked me what I thought.'

'I could always say I overslept. Or that British Rail screwed up. It wouldn't be the first time.'

No one spoke.

At length Bognor said, 'You said a helicopter had been found at the Norton Fitzpriors air base.'

'*Jawohl*,' said Molly.

Monica scowled.

'Anybody in it?'

'My sources say no.'

'Hmmm.' Bognor swilled some of his coffee around his mouth and thought. Eventually he said, 'This is absolutely off the record, unattributable, for your eyes only, top secret, confidential, cross your eyes and hope to die.'

'Guide's honour,' said Molly.

'If you'll excuse me, I think I'd better go and pack,' said Monica. She smiled one of her most notorious lemon sorbet smiles at Molly. 'Lovely seeing you again,' she said. The exit itself was also from the fast-freeze shelf. One or two of the solitary sales reps glanced up as she passed but immediately looked back at their tablecloths in shock.

'Sorry, Simon,' said Molly, putting a hand on his, 'have I caused a little tiff?'

Simon regarded her astonishingly long and amazingly crimson fingernails.

'No,' he said, 'not really.'

Molly smiled the knowing smile of one who had spent much of her private and professional life summing up other people's marriages. Prolonged observation had deterred her from trying the experience at first hand. It was not for want of opportunities.

'Good,' she said. 'You were saying . . .?'

Bognor told her about their visit to the Haven. Not quite knowing why, he left out the bit about Glatt. He didn't want Glatt in the *Globe* even off the record and unattributable.

'Good story,' she said. 'So Andover Strobe has become a CIA stooge?'

'It looks like it,' said Bognor. 'It reminds me of one of Arthur Green's novels – everyone seems to have his or her price.'

'It doesn't sound as if Glopff or Hastings are in it for the money,' said Molly. 'Glopff is presumably a professional agent and Hastings appears to have unfulfilled literary ambitions. Ambitions Hemlock wasn't able to indulge. Come to that Strobe gives the impression of being more interested in power than loot. So it's not like a Green novel. I agree the Green oeuvre is concerned entirely with lust, money and airport lounges but I don't think this is the same thing at all. But it's still a good story. I wonder if they'll run Strobe to earth?'

'He's not exactly unobtrusive,' said Bognor, 'but Bumstead is such an oaf I wouldn't put it past him.'

'I wish the Midgelys had murdered someone.' Molly lit another cheroot. 'I feel a lot of ill will towards them, but there you are. How much of this stuff can I use without losing you your job?'

Bognor sighed. 'I sometimes think losing my job would be the best thing for me,' he said, 'but if that happens I'll probably lose my wife too and I don't actually want that. Oh, just proceed with care. Talk to the fuzz and see what they're prepared to say officially. They can hardly deny having mounted an operation at Reckitt Magna. They made enough noise about it. The locals can't have missed it. See what bromide they put out, then embellish according to what I've told you. You can certainly say that Megaword are, effectively, making a bid for the commercially viable bit of the British book industry and I think you could say that they're doing it with official American backing.'

'And what about the Green factoid?'

'How much do you know?'

Molly put on a poker face. 'Not a lot,' she said. 'If I did it would have been in my story. How does it tie in with the fishing trip?'

'I haven't worked that out.'

'It really is non-fiction?'

'Yes.'

'Libellous?'

137

Bognor considered. 'The principal character is dead. Beyond libel. Ditto quite a few others. But some may still be alive in which case there's certainly a potential libel.'

'Can't you be a little more specific?'

'It's traitors and double agents. You know, the Chapman Pincher–Nigel West school of writing. After Philby and Blunt, who next?'

'Lord Rothschild?'

'No, no.' Bognor flicked toast crumbs off his tie and grinned. Molly did bring out his innate sense of mischief. So did most hacks. He had enjoyed his brief foray into journalism, investigating the death of that drunken diarist, St John Derby. Mad, arguably; bad, unquestionably; dangerous to know, well, yes, on balance; but journalists were entertaining people to hang around with. At least those of the old school were – the ones before the age of the Cellnet phone and the lap computer. 'Wrong sex,' he said. 'The newest double agent is not a bloke.'

Molly thought hard. 'The Queen Mother,' she said at last.

'Good try,' said Bognor, 'but I'm afraid my lips are now sealed. I've said more than enough.'

'Are you going fishing with Arthur and Romany?' she asked.

'I might lurk,' said Bognor, 'just to see what happens.'

'I'll be lurking myself,' said Molly. 'Maybe we'll meet in the shadows.'

And she effected an exit, left, with as much period theatricality as her entrance.

Bognor carefully spread the last slice of toast and pondered.

Any normal conscientious subordinate would, of course, have done as he was told by his boss, but Bognor was not like that. He had reached a time of life when it scarcely mattered whether he threw caution to the winds or not. It was plain that he was not going to what his teachers and tutors had always referred to as 'the top'. The older he got the less clear he was where the elusive top was to be found. Observing other more energetic climbers it always seemd to him that the top was a chimera permanently situated beyond the next horizon. In any case Bognor was so obviously marooned in the foothills just above base camp that there was no point in pretending otherwise.

Parkinson would be magnificently furious. No doubt about that. But when it came to the crunch Bognor would be difficult to sack. For breaking the Official Secrets Act and talking to the press, maybe – though not automatically. Cf. Clive Ponting. For being late back to the office, hardly. If Parkinson tried that Bognor would get himself taken up by the union. Become a *cause célèbre*.

And his curiosity was aroused. The more this case progressed the more potential villains emerged. Strobe, Glopff and Hastings on the run; Capstick and Warrington in clink; Arthur Green and Romany Flange about to get on a boat under pseudonymous disguise; Bumstead and Glatt thrashing about the county with the anti-terrorist squad. Things must surely be moving towards some sort of resolution. Could he miss the denouement while sitting frustrated on a slow train home?

He could not.

It should have been easy to apprehend a maverick publisher with an enormous head and a pair of supergame legs but Strobe proved elusive. They sought him here, they sought him there . . . Bumstead ranted; Glatt's smile tightened. A watch was put on the airports and the Channel ports and a Special Branch posse in riding macs and brown felt hats, like characters from an old 'B' movie, called on the Strobe offices in Elysium Wharf on the Isle of Dogs where they upset a number of secretaries but found nothing. They took away some unsolicited typescripts and some light blue sketches for Glatt's erotic bestiary just to show that they were not to be trifled with.

'As a new author of Strobe's I feel particularly aggrieved,' said Glatt, sitting in the back of an unmarked constabulary Rover with Bumstead but speaking to himself rather than the DCI who could not be expected to understand. 'If I'd realised he was going to do a deal with Megaword I'd have gone elsewhere. Or maybe I wouldn't. One mustn't allow one's politics to interfere with one's poetry. Or vice versa.'

The poet fingered the shaft of the Navajo throwing knife he always carried in the special pocket in the uppers of his goatskin boots. It had killed more than one man already – several, in fact. But never yet a publisher.

Monica saw the car as it prowled aimlessly down the promenade. Years of experience had taught her to recognise such vehicles almost by instinct. As it waited for the red light to change she pretended to be checking the window display of the nearest shop front and contemplated the two men on the back seat. Their expressions were familiar to her. She had become accustomed to it after years of marriage. It was obvious to her, if not to others, that although they were trying to appear in charge of the situation they were actually all at sea. They had not found Andover Strobe and did not know where to look.

There had, naturally, been a row at the Goose and Goblet. Monica, fed up to the teeth with Byfleet-next-the-Sea, apprehensive about being kidnapped again, reluctant to see her husband playing fast and loose with his pension, was determined on a home run. The more she exhorted, cajoled and erupted, the more obstinate Bognor had become. Her fury was made worse by the sudden discovery that her engagement ring was missing. The paradox was that had she been wearing it she would probably have torn it off and thrown it at him, but missing it she missed it. It was Victorian, semi-precious stone (garnet), bought together in the Brighton lanes. She noticed the loss when she had gone upstairs to pack.

Under the bed? In the loo? Handbag? No. She could not have taken it off at the Haven. Nor in the Winter Gardens. She distinctly remembered having it on the night before Hemlock was murdered because he had admired it. 'What a perfectly charming ring, me dear,' he had said, lifting her hand to examine it and planting a slobbery kiss on her fingers. *Quel* creep!

The row ended in a stroppy agreement to diverge. Monica was to go home on the 9.10; Simon to play truant in the hope of seeing mysteries solved. Monica made a detour on her way to the station, hoping that someone or other might still be at Hemlocks and that she might find the garnet ring there lying where she had left it. It was a long chance but the only chance she could conjure up.

This was why she happened to be on the promenade when the Bumstead–Glatt limo drove by and paused at the lights. The day was still bright and crisp. She shivered slightly, partly from cold, partly from something more abstract and ethereal. It was this side of fear but the far side of apprehension. Rows with her husband tended to make her uneasy. They were usually resolved quite fast but they were infrequent these days and they worried her when they did come. She was always afraid one of them would fall under a bus before a reconciliation could be effected. She would hate to leave a bad taste behind. Nor did she relish arriving at the Pearly Gates as an estranged wife. She felt St Peter would lack sympathy. Superstitious old duck, Monica.

The police car smoothed off like an unguided missile, predatory but powerless, target unidentified. Monica stayed for a moment, gazing at what appeared to a windowful of World War Two army surplus women's knickers, and then moved on towards the dead publisher's house.

Was it her imagination, or had it acquired a morgue-like air? A shutter on the first floor had lost a hinge and dangled limp; there was a hole in the glass roof of the porte-cochère; a large dog turd disfigured the pavement outside; a black rim around the half-submerged basement windows served as a vivid obituary notice to Hemlocks' deceased owner. She stood briefly at the door, swallowed hard and pressed the bell. A longish pause. Somewhere in the distance she thought she heard a door bang. Footsteps? Couldn't be. Imagination playing tricks. Pity, the engagement ring would have to become past history. Insurance would pay for another. Not as nice, not the Real McCoy. She and Simon would go on a sentimental outing to the Brighton lanes and find a substitute. Something identical would be four times the price and out of reach but they would find something acceptable. She was clever in shops like that. Had an eye for neglected goodies. Could bargain, too. She sighed and was about to turn away when there was a buzz. A voice, metallic and unrecognisable, emanated from the grille.

'Hello. Who's there?'

The keys, thought Monica, remembering a late night at the Tower of London, the Queen's keys. Aloud, she said, 'It's Monica Bognor. I'm sorry to disturb you. It's just, I think I left something behind the other day. A ring. And I wonder if I might . . . I mean . . .' She wondered why she was so uncharacteristically flustered and incoherent.

'Just a moment,' said the voice. There was a click and the buzzing stopped.

Again she waited. Better not be too long or she'd miss the train. The next wasn't for two hours. Oh, well, what was a couple of hours in life's rich what-have-you? A thousand ages in His sight was just an evening gone and all that. Where would Simon be now? In trouble, no doubt. Just so long as he didn't get shot at. He was so stubborn. One day the luck would run out and he would get seriously hurt. If only he'd gone into merchant banking or prep school headmastership. A nice cosy job at Morgan Grenfell with long lunches and gullible boardrooms. Too late now. Oh, what was become of youth and promise and . . . there was a snap, crackle, pop and the disembodied voice said, 'You'd better come in, Mrs Bognor.' Another click and then the buzz which meant the door was off the latch. She pushed, tentatively, and it gave way. She stepped forward and into the hall. It was gloomy dark and as the door clicked shut behind her she strained to make out the shadowy figures lined up to welcome her. They were all too familiar. In the centre, the big-headed, disabled shape of Andover Strobe in his chair, and flanking him Hastings and Glopff. Glopff held her little Derringer, Hastings a large military .38.

They all smiled.

'Mrs Bognor,' said Strobe, eyes opaque and chilled as ever, thin lips stretched just wide enough to reveal the tips of teeth, 'this is an unexpected pleasure . . . but you're very, very welcome.'

Bognor was also fazed by connubial discord. It made him mutter. 'Silly cow!' he repeated to himself as he descended the stairs of the Goose, 'if only she'd listen. I've never known a

142

woman interrupt as much as she does. And hector. Bloody back-seat drive through life. "Do this, do that, don't do this, don't do that." Yack, yack, yack and who pays the mortgage, I'd like to know? Just answer that, Mrs Bognor. It may not be much but it's kept you in After Eights and Pretty Polly tights for most of your adult life. I dare say you could have married someone with more money but you've never gone short so it's a bit ripe . . . Ooops, sorry!'

He had almost *bouleverséed* the Midgelys.

It was a narrow staircase of the sort one finds in pubs. Sharp bends and steep steps. Little room to pass without a degree of physical proximity that people as fastidious as the Midgelys found upsetting. You had to touch. Touching strangers wasn't nice.

'Oh, hello!' said Bognor, inhaling Cynthia's heavy aroma of Chanel and talc. 'Bognor, Board of Trade, I thought you'd left town with the circus.'

They stared back as if in mild shock.

'Oh, Mr Bognor,' said Wilfred. 'We wrote you a letter.'

Bognor couldn't help noticing the 'we'. It could be that they did everything together; it could be that it was a regal derivative. He wondered if Cynthia was much given to saying 'my husband and I'.

'My husband and I wrote to you,' said Cynthia, confirming his suspicions, 'but if you're still here you won't have got it.'

'No,' said Bognor, 'I am so I haven't.'

It wasn't the best place for a discussion and Bognor said so. They adjourned to the foyer. It was still cramped – not much more than a passage but there were a few chairs. They sat.

'I thought everyone would have gone home by now,' said Bognor. 'Nothing here but unpleasant memories.'

'We're addressing the Local Literary Guild,' said Cynthia with a simper of pride. '"The Role of the Royal Biographer in Twentieth-century Literature."'

'Gosh,' said Bognor. He remembered that Glatt had used the local Lit Soc as an excuse. It gave him pause for a frown.

'We've been ever so worried,' said Wilfred.

'We don't think poor Audrey Hemlock killed herself,' said Cynthia.

'Why not?' asked Bognor.

'Writers are very good judges of character, Mr Bognor. Wilfred and I couldn't be biographers without having a real intuition into what makes people tick.'

Bognor thought of *Good Queen Bess* and *The Royal Family Bedside Book*, swallowed hard and nodded.

'Absolutely,' he said.

'Anyway,' continued Cynthia, 'she'd been on very good form that morning at breakfast. Full of plans for the future. All that sort of thing.'

'She could just have been putting a brave face on it,' said Bognor; 'being British.'

'Oh, no,' said Wilfred, 'that wasn't Audrey's style. Not her way of doing things at all. You could always tell what was in Audrey's mind. At least, Cynthia and I could.'

'And it wasn't suicide,' said Cynthia.

'So,' said Bognor, glancing surreptitiously at his watch. He had a rendezvous with Molly Mortimer and her fisherman. He didn't want to miss it. 'What happened to her if it wasn't suicide?'

'Well,' Cynthia leaned forward and dropped her voice to a shade over whisper, 'the story is that Romany Flange came back from London, went straight up to Audrey's room and found her dead.'

'Yes,' said Bognor, 'that's the official line. It's what Romany Flange told Bumstead. It's on the files.'

'But it's not true,' said Wilfred. For once he looked quite fierce.

'How do you mean, "not true"?'

'Simply not true,' said Cynthia. 'We saw Green's car. You can't miss it. It's an old gold Lagonda, registration GRN 1. Vulgar and ostentatious just like his ghastly hero, Lance Remington.'

'And singularly unlike Arthur Green himself,' said Bognor.

'Anyway,' Cynthia looked disapproving, 'it's unmistakable. He drives it surprisingly fast, too. I think,' she lowered her voice yet further, fluttered her false eyelashes and gave a girlish giggle, 'I think he thinks he *is* Lance Remington when he's driving the Lagonda. Would you believe, he calls it "Daisy" or "Old Girl" when he's being familiar.'

'Flange went to London with us and Capstick in his Rolls,' said Bognor, thinking.

'Well, she didn't come back with him,' said Cynthia. 'She's admitted that. She got a lift with Arthur Green. And they were in Byfleet a full half hour before they were officially back. We saw them drive down the prom. You couldn't miss them.'

'I see,' said Bognor. 'Can you prove it?'

'We both saw them.' Cynthia looked at Wilfred. Wilfred nodded. Miranda Howard turned back to Bognor and nodded in unison.

'What exactly are you suggesting?' Bognor guessed what they were driving at but he wanted to hear it from their own lips.

Cynthia took a deep breath. 'I know it's a dreadful thing to say,' she said, 'but we think they came back early and murdered Audrey Hemlock. Poisoned her. We think one of them held her while the other forced down the overdose of sleeping tablets. Then half an hour later Romany Flange "discovered" her.'

'It's a theory.' Bognor scratched the back of his neck. 'But I can't see it's much more.'

'I bet there's forensic evidence,' said Wilfred, 'if they bother to look. But they won't. It's all too cut and dried. They won't take the trouble. Much easier to record a suicide. The circumstances make it all so plausible.'

'But why?' Bognor was by no means sure that Romany Flange and Arthur Green belonged to the murdering classes. Particularly as this killing involved premeditation and a coolness of execution that required exceptionally cold blood. Still, one never knew. Murder was a funny old game.

'Romany's very ambitious. She obviously wanted to take control of Big Books. With Vernon out of her way Audrey was the only obstacle left.' To Cynthia it seemed to be clear-cut and straightforward.

'But, with respect, Mrs Midgely, even in the City people who want to gain control of companies don't go around murdering

145

the chairmen. There are more conventional ways of going about these things.'

'This isn't the City, Mr Bognor,' said Cynthia. 'This is the world of books.'

'Sounds as if some people are beginning to believe their own plots,' said Bognor. He suddenly felt very weary. 'I'll try to get the forensic people to have a proper look,' he said, 'but it's awfully thin. So you saw Green's Lagonda half an hour or so before they say they arrived. They could have stopped off to get the papers or buy a coffee. It simply isn't enough. Unless there's some corroborating evidence. Is there?'

The Midgelys shuffled their feet.

'Well, thanks anyway,' he said. 'If there's anything else . . .'

The Midgelys looked at each other. They seemed embarrassed.

'I don't think it's really relevant,' said Wilfred.

Cynthia shook her head. 'In a case like this everything's relevant. Isn't that so, Mr Bognor?'

'You could say so,' said Bognor. His mind was on other things.

'We think Dr Belgrave has been behaving quite oddly.'

'Oddly?'

'Oddly. She's been ever so snappish with us and with other people. And several of us heard her shouting at Vernon the day he was killed. And she got very angry with Romany Flange, too.'

Bognor nodded. 'I understand she hasn't been at all happy recently,' he said. 'I think I know some of the reasons.'

'We,' Wilfred sounded very conspiratorial indeed, 'we've thought Dr Belgrave peculiar for quite some time now.'

'You have?' Bognor conceded that Dr Belgrave was not usual, but it sounded as if the Midgely team harboured a grudge.

'She gave us a lot of trouble with Vernon,' said Cynthia.

'Trouble?'

'She's obsessed with sex,' said Wilfred, with a prim twitch of the lip.

'It makes her rich and famous,' said Bognor, 'so one can hardly blame her. If I were a rude person I could say you were

146

obsessed with people who happen to be royal.'

'That's not at all the same thing, as you know perfectly well.' Cynthia did not sound as put out as the words themselves implied. 'And what Wilfred is trying to say is that Ann Belgrave was very peculiar about sex *and* royalty.'

'How so?'

'She was always trying to persuade Vernon and us to make our books more what she liked to call "sexually explicit". She even wanted to combine with us to produce "Sex and the Royal Family" or some such filth by Ann Belgrave and Miranda Howard. In that order. The idea!'

Bognor assumed that the Miranda Howard attitude to sex and the Royal Family was like the pre-Swinging Sixties attitude to the Royals and practically everything, particularly smoking and drinking. Royal people didn't smoke and drink in those days and couldn't be photographed with a glass in their hand or a fag between their lips. In a Miranda Howard book royal babies arrived 'By Appointment', flown in by special storks from the Norland Nanny Agency. The worst thing a royal personage could do between the sheets in a *Royal Family Bedside Book* was to snore.

'I suppose you take the Barbara Cartland line on sex.' Bognor smiled to imply the condescension of one who is no stranger to steamy animal sexual acts though if the truth be told he was, if not virginal, at least orthodox to a degree that would have been, before AIDS, quite shaming.

'Ba Cartland', said Cynthia, 'is so terribly, terribly right. The whole point about the Queen and her family is that they are all desperately romantic. They are all about love and nothing about sex. That is what Wilfred and I try to convey.'

'Dr Belgrave wanted you to convey something quite different?'

'Absolutely.' Wilfred nodded. 'So much so that we began to think she might be some sort of red. I mean it was almost as if she wanted to discredit the Royal Family. She kept going on about the Duke of Clarence being Jack the Ripper. Things like that. She had a whole lot of stories about Prince Philip and . . . well I won't go into all that.'

'She said we "avoided the real issues" when we talked about

Kurt Hahn and Gordonstoun,' said Cynthia. 'She said short trousers and cold baths were sexual. She thought Freud would have had theories about them. To start with, Wilfred and I just treated it all as some sort of joke but recently it had gone beyond that. I expect you remember that outrageous book that came out last year – the one implying that Queen Victoria, well, that she and Albert had, well . . . you know what I mean. Well, as soon as that came out she wanted to do something similar about the Queen herself. I mean, good grief!'

Cynthia subsided.

'It's true,' said Wilfred 'She was making herself a perfect pest. And we weren't the only ones who were having trouble. She'd been having a go at Danvers Warrington. She wanted him to put more sex into his stuff too. Aphrodisiac qualities of Bordeaux as measured against Burgundy. She saw sex in everything . . . She even produced what she said was Winston Churchill's . . . well, a sort of cellar book. It was a record of everything he drank. She tried to get Warrington to produce an edited version. Warrington took expert advice and said it was a forgery. Jolly good forgery but a forgery all the same.'

'Hmmm,' said Bognor. Somewhere in the back of his skull a burglar alarm was beginning to sound. 'Are you sure?'

'It's what Warrington told us,' said Cynthia. 'There's no reason for him to make it up.'

'Not that I can see,' said Wilfred.

'Nor me,' agreed Bognor. 'And you put all this in your letter?'

'Yes.' They spoke together, as Miranda Howard.

Odd couple, thought Bognor. 'Well, thanks,' he said.

They all stood, preparatory to going their separate ways.

'To be perfectly frank,' said Cynthia, 'this has all been a terrible shock, but in a way it's only the final straw.'

'The final straw?'

Wilfred gave that prim twitch again. 'You're an educated sort of chap,' he said, 'so you'll understand. For some time now Cynthia and I have been unhappy with what one can only describe as the vulgarity of what Vernon and indeed Romany were doing. Jacket designs; promotions; sales campaigns. Vulgar's the only word.'

'You weren't thinking of moving to Andover Strobe?' Bognor wondered if yet another motive was about to break out from the undergrowth.

'Good gracious, no!' Both halves of Miranda Howard looked thunderstruck. 'We're thinking seriously about going to somewhere that's still a gentlemanly house where you can rely on their tact and discretion and a certain refinement,' said Wilfred.

'Don't breathe a word to anyone,' said Cynthia, who gave the impression of having removed a weight from her mind, 'but we're negotiating with some of the very few gentlemen left in British publishing. We think we'll be making an announcement before very long.'

'It's Macmillan actually,' said Wilfred, 'but don't tell anyone.'

Bognor nodded sagely and left deep in thought. He had decided that he was almost certainly going fishing.

SEVEN

Bognor found the *Globe*'s Literary Editor and her young fisherman sitting on a plank supported between two upturned lobster pots. They were within a loud hail of the Mermaid's Tail and they were drinking coffee laced with rum. The fisherman had brought a thermos of hot Nescafé. Molly, with the typical resource of the seasoned newshound (newsbitch? mused Bognor) had procured a half bottle of Captain Morgan's.

'This is Trevor,' said Molly.

'Hello, Trevor,' said Simon.

Trevor and Simon shook hands. Simon was depressingly aware of his limp and clammy shake compared with Trevor's stiff dry one; also of his shifty, rheumy eyes, compared with Trevor's clear, unwavering blue ones. He sensed Trevor's tattoo rippling under his Arran sweater and comforted himself a little with the thought that he had an Oxford degree and an index-linked pension (provided that wasn't blown on today's little excursion).

'I was telling Trev', said Molly, 'that we want to stow away on this morning's little joy-ride. He's upped me to a hundred quid each. I think we can stick on that.'

'If he'll take a cheque.' Bognor was not happy about this. He saw little chance of being able to charge it to expenses. The fare represented two gourmet dinners with his beloved. A stiff price to pay.

Trev nodded.

'No funny stuff, mind,' he said. 'I don't want no funny stuff. You just stay where I tell you and no funny stuff. I don't want my passengers upset.'

'I bet they're not paying the same price as we are,' said Bognor.

'Maybe not,' said Trev, 'but that's not the point.'

'Oh,' said Bognor. He glanced at Molly who nodded.

'We'll be good as lambkins,' she said. 'Nary a peep nor a cheep.'

'Right then.' Trev drained his rummy coffee and stood up, smacking the tops of his thigh-length waders. Molly looked at him with lust in her eyes. 'We'd better stow you away before your friends turn up.'

And he led them along the stone quayside to a rusting iron ladder which descended vertically down the harbour wall. The three of them clambered down this without mishap, Bognor cursing inwardly and wishing he'd worn boots. At the bottom there were half a dozen boats moored alongside each other. All were grubby, rusty and stank of diesel and dead herring. Bognor retched. Perhaps Parkinson knew best after all. This was silly and not even in the line of duty. Rather, he reminded himself, the reverse.

'Hammond Innes or Alistair Maclean territory,' said Molly, nimbly negotiating some coils of rope on the deck of the first boat. 'Odd that Hemlock had no Big Boat Books on his list. Sea stories can be ginormous.'

Bognor was too engrossed to respond. The decks were slippery with fishblood, engine oil, slops, drizzle and detritus. Their destination was obviously the furthest away of the boats and he was not as nifty on his pins as he'd been in the days when he had played inside right for the college's second hockey eleven. It took all his concentration to stay upright.

'So this is the *Saucy Sue*,' exclaimed Molly, finally, allowing herself to be handed over the low guardrail of a grubby little tub which had once been painted dark blue but was now so mottled with rust and sea-gunge that it resembled tricolour batik. For a smoker and drinker of a certain age she seemed depressingly fit. Bognor was wheezing horribly, and regretting the whole enterprise.

'You can go below,' said Trevor. 'I'll tell Mr and Mrs Smith they can't go down there. No problem.'

'Will we be able to hear what they say?' asked Bognor, looking out to sea and noticing the white horses with a degree of apprehension.

'She's full of holes,' said Trevor. 'No problem.'

Bognor did not feel optimistic either about the holes on board or about the cavalier way in which Trevor was given to saying 'no problem'. No matter that he had high cheekbones, the athletic gait of one of nature's matelots and more than a hint of steel beneath the boyish charm, his boat reminded Bognor of a neglected colander. And the skin stretched tight over those distinctive cheekbones had a suspiciously high colour which looked as if it owed as much to rum-laced coffee as it did to wind and weather. And even at the best of times Bognor was not one of the world's great sailors.

They made another descent, this time through a hatchway. Bognor supposed it should be called a cabin though it was simply an ill-lit space. The smell was bad. It was damp. The water could be heard slapping the side.

'I'll be going ashore, then,' Trevor called down at them, 'to pick up the passengers. You'd best not smoke on account of the fumes. And remember, I don't want no trouble.'

They listened to his stout sea boots clomping off across the decking towards the harbour wall.

'Cod liver oil!' said Molly.

'I beg your pardon?' Bognor was regretting his cooked breakfast.

'Reminds me of school and the sanatorium,' said Molly; 'that smell.'

Bognor closed his eyes.

'Able Roger to Charlie Tango, Able Roger to Charlie Tango, I say again Able Roger to Charlie Tango.'

The sudden crackle of the police radio jerked Bumstead and Merlin Glatt out of their depressed and jaded somnolence. They were on the coast road about five miles north of Byfleet-next-the-Sea, not knowing what to do but neither man caring to admit it to the other.

The man in the front passenger seat acknowledged the call, telling Able Roger that Charlie Tango heard him loud and clear.

'Message from a Mr Murray to Lord George Byron.'

'Aha!' breathed Glatt. His nostrils dilated slightly, his pulse quickened. 'The foe!' he exclaimed. 'They come! They come!'

Bumstead gave him a ferociously old-fashioned look.

'Message reads,' said Able Roger, 'Thracian trireme proceeding Byfleetwards. Corsair closing. Chariot of fire RV with Byron zero nine-thirty hours. Map reference . . .'

Glatt pinpointed the spot on the Ordnance Survey map on his lap.

'Message for my Murray ex Byron,' he said. 'Gallant Company goes merrily.'

'You what?' said the front-seat sergeant.

Glatt repeated the message with frost in his voice, circled the map reference and passed it to the driver.

'You'll need to put your foot on it,' he said. He turned to Bumstead. 'If you don't mind dropping me off, Charles, I'll put you in the picture some time this afternoon when this little lot has been sorted out. I rather hope it will all be finished in time for me to do my bit at the Byfleet Literary Guild.' He fingered the reassuring holster bulge under his armpit.

'Right,' said Bumstead, aware that any pretence of authority was long gone but determined to keep up a semblance of an appearance. 'Carry on, driver.'

If, for the second time in twenty-four hours, she was the victim of a kidnap, Monica had to confess that it was being handled in an extremely civilised manner.

She, Strobe and Marlene Glopff sat in the library drinking Lapsang Souchong from Hemlocks' prettiest porcelain. Hastings buttled somewhere off stage.

'I'm terribly afraid', said Strobe, 'that the time will come when we're going to have to use you as an insurance policy, a bargaining counter. As you will have realised after last night there is a distinct possibility of high velocity lead flying about. Too, too terribly tiresome. But with you at our side − or more probably at our front − I hope that sort of unpleasantness can be avoided.' He sipped and smiled.

'Wasn't it rather rash? Coming here, I mean.' She too sipped and smiled. If being cool was the name she would match them sip for sip and smile for smile.

'The obvious is so often the least expected,' said Strobe. 'This is the last place that Bumstead and his men would even think of looking. I had my doubts about Mr Glatt but he's not as clever as he thinks he is. At least not when it comes to this sort of thing. Isn't that so, Marlene poppet?'

Marlene purred.

'I'm most concerned at the moment,' said Strobe, 'about the Butskell-Godunov diaries. Indeed it seems that this has become a subject of almost universal concern. At least . . .' he smiled at Monica as if to imply that she might have more privileged information, 'that's what my sources tell me.'

'Do you fancy publishing them?' asked Monica. 'Or,' and here she glanced at Marlene, 'do you have a more political use for them?'

'I'd prefer not to answer that,' said Strobe. 'In the unlikely event that you get out of this alive I would prefer not to have you repeating too many incriminating remarks in court.'

Monica shrugged. It hadn't seriously occurred to her that she was going to come to an untimely end in this escapade. That was the sort of thing that happened in the Billion Lire Breakfast and the Million Dollar Martini. In real life — hers, anyway — death was by road accident, stroke, heart attack, cancer, old age. She supposed AIDS would have to be added to the list, though neither she nor her husband was bisexual or on hard drugs. Murder was a non-starter.

'Your husband perplexes me, Mrs Bognor.' Strobe did indeed look a touch mystified. 'He seems only to be interested in the identity of whoever killed Mr and Mrs Hemlock.'

'He had other interests,' said Monica, piqued. 'He was writing a Mauve Paper on publishing for the Government. Also a book about the Department he works for. But once the murders had been committed they became his main concern. Naturally.'

'Not "naturally" at all.' Strobe caressed the suede-lined arms of his chair. 'The least important aspect of this entire affair is sudden death. To be concerned with the fate of Vernon and Audrey is pure sentiment.' A tiny chink of genuine curiosity opened up in the milky eyes. 'I suppose he'll be concerned

154

about your death, Mrs Bognor? If it happens.'

'I suppose so.'

'It happens to all of us sooner or later. Not something to make a fuss about.'

Monica was saved from having to respond by the sudden incursion of the butler carrying a Cellnet telephone. Had he still been in the service of the late Vernon Hemlock he would have brought it on a silver salver but now he came in without knocking, carrying the phone nonchalantly in one hand.

'Boss, boss,' he said, handing it to Marlene.

'Hi, Hugh,' said Marlene, chewing on some tofu chewing gum, a packet of which lay open on the Sheraton library steps, 'what's cooking?'

Evidently quite a lot was cooking. Marlene listened and chewed and grunted. Finally she said, 'OK, Hugh, I read you. We'll do what has to be done.' Then she gave the phone back to Hastings, picked the gum from her mouth and threw it in the fire. 'Shit!' she said, pleasantly. 'We have problems.'

Below deck on the *Saucy Sue* may not have been on a par with the Black Hole of Calcutta nor yet the hold of a slaver but it was a far cry from the saloon of Hemlock's *Lady Audrey* or Strobe's *First Option*, both moored permanently at Cannes. Bognor's knees had begun to play up in middle-age and after the first five minutes both of them started to ache. A little later the ache became punctuated with staccato stabs. He tried groaning but Molly told him to shut up and be a man. The smell was ghastly. Molly still had the half bottle of rum but after one swig Bognor decided that alcohol would only make matters worse. Molly's breath — alcohol, cheroot, coffee and lack of sleep — was a serious offence in the already fetid atmosphere. He tried humming military airs to himself and imagined what it must have been like at Rorke's Drift.

Presently they heard voices and the banging of feet.

'Getting fair choppy out there,' said Trevor.

Bognor's heart sank. The news was unwelcome. Reception, on the other hand, was excellent. Both he and Molly had a number of spy-hole chinks and crevices. These not only allowed a view but also seemed to enhance hearing. Voices from on deck came through loud and clear. Through his number-one hole he could also see all six legs from the knees down. Galumphing sea boots for Trevor; moderately sensible brown Veldtshoen for Arthur Green; hopelessly inappropriate sling-backs for Romany Flange. All he could see of Trevor was his waterproof waders; Green's shoes were topped by grey flannel; La Flange was in patterned black stockings. Good calves, he thought.

'Not too rough, I hope,' said Romany. 'I'm not exactly the world's greatest sailor.'

'Don't worry about it.' Green's voice sounded less beige and damp than usual. 'We don't have far to go.'

'I suppose we have to do this.' Romany's voice sounded distinctly quaverish. Uncharacteristic. 'It seems so terribly final.'

'Listen . . .' Green's voice was suddenly drowned by the growl and sputter of an engine failing to ignite. Between two failures snatches of sentence floated down to Bognor and Molly Mortimer. '. . . The only way to tell the story . . .' '*Glasnost* has changed everything . . .' Then, at the third try, the ancient engine caught. Trev revved, then throttled back so that it idled away to a gentle lawnmower throb which rattled every last bolt and rivet and drowned all speech. Bognor cursed.

Presently they heard the clump of Trevor's boots above them. He must have been casting off because a few moments later the engine picked up power, the bows pointed out to sea and they headed for the harbour mouth. The two stowaways gazed out through a porthole as the harbour wall slipped past and the boat began to roll.

The *Saucy Sue*'s engines seemed to get noisier, a sharp metallic clatter mingling with the softer, regular, resonant throb that had gone before. Bognor frowned, strained hard to catch the origin of the altered note, exclaimed: 'Listen!'

They both froze and gradually the new sound drowned out the old, rising to a crescendo, then starting to fade and drifting away to the east. Peering through his porthole, smeared now with the froth from scudding, salty spray, Bognor saw a dull

156

grey insect shuddering overhead, wing whirring above it like a whirligig. The glass was too dirty, the weather too gurly for him to distinguish any markings. In the sky above the quintessential English seaside resort it had, even when Big Books were at stake, to be one of ours.

'Chopper,' he said laconically. 'I think you may be going to get a story.'

Molly scribbled in her reporter's note book and almost laughed.

'Makes a change from Crime Writers' Association annual dinners,' she said.

Byron had made the RV with the Chariot. Now, sitting in the flimsy dragonfly a few hundred feet above sea level, he braced himself against the bucking of the wind and attempted to train the Zeiss field glasses on the horizon. They were Abwehr surplus — cumbersome but effective. Good for the image.

Immediately below them a tubby litle fishing boat nosed out of the narrow entrance to Byfleet harbour. The helicopter pilot, an angular Aberdonian, turned the whirlybird on its side for a couple of seconds so that both of them could look down on the vessel through their bulbous perspex globe. One man in the wheelhouse; two matchstick figures crouched in its lee.

Jock Cameron chuckled into the mouthpiece.

Glatt winced.

'Hope they've taken their Kwells,' said Jock, flipping the machine back on to an even keel, letting the nose drop and heading off towards Denmark, leaving the *Saucy Sue* bobbing about astern.

Glatt pressed the Zeiss glasses back to his eyes.

'"I saw the new moon late yestreen,"' he murmured,
'"Wi' the auld moon in her arm;
   And if we gang to sea, master,
   I fear we'll come to harm."'

Parkinson pursed his lips. His man was not on the 9.10 to Bradleigh Parkway. Nor Mrs Bognor. Yet they had checked out of the Goose and Goblet. The man Bumstead was clearly an oaf. The computer search on Merlin Glatt was far from conclusive.

'I'm not a bit happy about it. Not a bit,' he said.

The Air Vice-Marshal in Northwood had been shifty to the point of insolence; Hereford had barely given him the time of day; Sir Pendragon Star at Six had talked loosely of a shindig at sea; Fitzroy at Five had hinted darkly, and disgracefully, that his department was on thin ice; the Cabinet office had been permanently engaged.

In a final throw he had instructed his secretary to call the Bognor home in London.

'Please speak after the beep,' she reported.

'Eeny, meeny, miny, mo,' he said, staring wistfully at the Homburg on the hat stand. 'You know, Miss Travers, young Bognor has got me into more trouble than the whole of the rest of the Special Investigations Department put together. Not since Harold Wilson was President of the Board of Trade has anyone caused us as much gratuitous angst. And that, Miss Travers, was before you were born.'

Miss Travers, a pert child of the sixties, could only dimple acquiescence. She had seen Bognor several times in the canteen and thought him seedy. Also a bit of a dirty old man. He had looked at her the way some older men did.

'I suppose', he continued, 'that I should man my desk in a manner befitting my age and station. On the other hand if the shit hits the fan I'll end up with egg on my face, no matter what. Wouldn't you say, Miss Travers?'

Miss Travers flinched. She was a low-level plant from Six with – unknown to Parkinson – a first in Oriental Languages. She didn't like people who talked dirty.

Parkinson seemed to consider for a moment. Then he jumped to his feet.

'Tell Transport I want the fastest wheels in the garage, Miss Travers. Front door, ninety seconds' time. I'll telephone later. Don't leave your post until I've called.'

And he picked up his Homburg and was gone.

The Strobe gang were arming. Monica had never seen so much

158

state-of-the-art weaponry outside the Richmond Odeon. Strobe himself, zipped into a natty Swiss flak jacket, had a gold-plated sub-machine gun, which he cradled in his lap, stroking it as if it was some sort of pet. That was the extent of his armament. Marlene Glopff and Hastings, however, had everything the well-dressed terrorist was wearing that year – a brace of handguns apiece, the very latest stun grenades, which homed in on people and chased them about, knives, rope, custom-built head masks with built-in anti-gas respirators, the lot.

'It's only bloody Byfleet,' said Monica, 'not Beirut.'

'If things pan out Byfleet could make Beirut look like the Hotel du Lac,' said Hastings, checking the cartridge on a nasty-looking little Walther and revealing an unexpected knowledge of Booker Prizes past. 'This thing's become bigger than all of us.'

'You must try to understand, my dear,' said Strobe, buckling on a lightweight kukri, 'that we stand for the dominance of the word. In the beginning was the word – you know that. Nowadays you have to be market-led. Where the market leads, the dynamics of enterprise inevitably follow. Which is the principal reason why Megaword must have Green and maybe even Flange.'

It seemed to Monica that she must be going mad. Neither Glopff nor Hastings seemed to find this gobbledegook very interesting, but neither of them seemed amazed or even depressed by it. Glopff was sitting in the lotus position breathing deeply and staring, probably at her inner mind. Hastings was having trouble with a shoelace which had got knotted.

'What are we going to do?' she asked.

'The secret of Big Books and Megawords', said Strobe, eyes dancing like milkshakes in the blender, 'is a crescendo of great violence. All is resolved in that penultimate climax. There is explosive violence and violently explosive sex. It is the sort of thing at which Arthur Green excels. Have you read *Last Supper*?'

He tested the blade of his knife with his thumb and smiled up at her. 'I dare say your reading is of a cosier kind?'

159

'More Proustian,' said Monica bolshily. 'What's *Last Supper*?'

'It's Green's Biggest Book,' said Hastings peering down the barrel of a gun. 'The Pope is kidnapped by extra-terrestrials and hidden in an abandoned brothel in the mountains of Nicaragua where Lance Remington discovers him and there's this KGB General who's infiltrated the Oval Office at the White House and in the end they set up this incredible banquet where the extra-terrestrials finally intend to assassinate the President of the USA *and* the General Secretary of the Soviet Communist Party only Lance Remington finds out just in time and discovers a magic formula which turns all the extra-terrestrials into green jelly but not before they manage to put a grenade under the bed in which—'

'Cool it!' said Marlene. 'Put that thing down, breathe deeply, raise and lower the arms as you inhale and exhale. I want to see that whole organism recharged. Think Total Body Breath.'

To Monica's surprise, Hastings, who had been looking dangerously supercharged, did as he was told. After a few deep breaths his high colour paled and his pupils seemed less dilated.

'You should read *Last Supper*,' said Glopff; 'it has great resonances. The KGB guy is called Juri Iscarovitch – like Judas, geddit? And the big shoot-out at the end is straight from the Book of Revelation. You know, there's a message there.'

'Subtext,' said Monica. She wondered what the subtext of the present situation was. The three of them were clearly under some form of instruction from what they chose to believe to be the CIA. But was it? Was it, perhaps, some maverick branch of the organisation, spinning away like a satellite which changes orbit. Was the President still in control? Had he ever been in control? Was there an Iscarovitch somewhere behind an arras? Was Strobe from outer space? His *Who's Who* entry said he was born in Romford but maybe that was cover. Monica wished she knew.

The Cellnet phone trilled again. Glopff listened, swore, and said, 'That's too bad. We'll have to pray the Brits head them off. Meanwhile get some kind of transport to the pierhead. Yeah, soonest.' She gave the phone back to Hastings. 'We have to move our asses,' she said. 'The rest of the world is a step ahead. Someone goofed at Langley.' She turned to Mrs Bognor. 'OK, Monica,' she said, 'off your butt.'

It was distinctly choppy in Byfleet Bay. Bognor remembered Hemlock's pretty little Bonington, the one of the schooner at sea. The ocean deep was so picturesque in poetry and prose and paint, he reflected, and so perfectly bloody in real life. The *Saucy Sue* was pitching and rolling like a barrel nearing the Niagara drop. It was impossible to hear conversation above the steady drum of the engine and the slap of the waves. The view from the porthole was spasmodic. Bognor felt like the great J. M. W. Turner, tied to the mast in the cause of art. Imprisoned below decks in the service of the Board of Trade might not have quite the same nobility of purpose or echoes of grandeur but the apparent imminence of a watery grave was none the less.

He braced himself against the heaving boat, tried to ignore his heaving stomach and said to Molly Mortimer, 'What's the plan?'

The Literary Editor seemed to be enjoying herself. No sign of sea-sickness, an enviable ability to roll with the punches – useful attributes for a hackette, however literary. She had also had the presence of mind to bring binoculars – not the showy, cumbersome sort of thing that Glatt favoured but discreet and ladylike, reminiscent of Glopff's little Derringer: a pair of Japanese Chinon Eight by Twenty-fours with a 5.50 field.

'Ship,' she said, suddenly, 'out there on the horizon. Not that far away. Big fishing boat by the look of it.'

Bognor tried to stand but sat down again very heavily, bruising a buttock on a nautical knob.

'What nationality?'

'Red, yellow and black flag with a strange device. Also more dishes and antennae than the TV Centre. Oh, I think I can read the lettering on the stern. Hang on! Not easy. Just a sec.' She paused, bracing her legs like an ancient sea dog in an ancient cigarette ad. 'Dolores something,' she said. 'Rostok. Dolores Iba . . . can't make it out, I'm afraid.'

'Dolores Ibarruri,' said Bognor. 'La Pasionaria. That terrible blood-thirsty Republican woman in the Spanish Civil War. Just

161

the sort of person the Warsaw Pact names its navy after. East German so-called fishing boat. Actually a spy ship under direct control of the KGB and never done any bona fide fishing in the whole of its life. Come to pick up a couple of sprats. Or maybe they'll turn out to be mackerel. If we're not extremely careful your Green factoid is going to end up as the lead title of this year's Russian State Publishing House's autumn list. I don't like it.'

The *Saucy Sue* lurched. Bognor's sense of impending doom became even more acute. He was not happy.

'Good story!' said the Literary Editor.

Byron's Chariot rendezvoused with HMS *Snapdragon*, a Floral Class Fishery Protection Vessel, about two miles east of the Houndstooth Rock. Glatt came down from the chopper swaying gently on the end of a rope like Peter Pan in the Barbican at Christmas. HMS *Snapdragon* was a poorly converted torpedo boat, long past her prime and with only slippery postage stamps of deck to aim at but Glatt landed on both feet, upright and well able to acknowledge the welcoming salute of *Snapdragon*'s commanding officer, a cadaverous but wily Cornishman, Lieutenant Dudley Tregarron. Tregarron's steely blue eyes spoke of hidden depths. He would be a useful port in a storm.

'Welcome aboard, sir,' he said to the poet.

Glatt smiled. 'You've made contact with La Pasionaria?'

Tregarron smiled back. He spoke most Russian and German dialects and had just finished a longish chat with the *Dolores Ibarruri*. They had talked freely about cod, Dynamo Kiev and the likely whereabouts of any British warships – in that order. The East Germans were under the impression that Tregarron was the commander of a deep sea trawler out of Minsk. 'By the way,' he said, 'may I say how much I admired "The Dartington Rhymes"? Not to mention "Box". I have a copy in my cabin. If, when this little show is over, you'd be good enough to inscribe them I'd be most awfully grateful.'

The poet inclined his head, flared his nostrils briefly and reverted to Action Man.

'How soon before we can make contact?'

'If her course holds, thirty-five to forty-five minutes.'

Glatt nodded. 'She's fishing in British waters.'

'Yes, sir.'

'And she's after a big catch. A literary catch. Not exactly a First Folio. But big stuff. She mustn't hook anything. You understand me?'

It was the Cornishman's turn to nod.

'I'd prefer nothing too heavy,' said Glatt. 'My masters don't want an international incident. No blood on these already troubled waters.'

'Aye, aye, sir.'

'"Books,"' said Glatt, '"like men their authors, have no more than one way of coming into the world, but there are ten thousand to go out of it, and return no more."'

'"There is nothing constant in this world but inconstancy", sir.' The Lieutenant had read English at Trinity, Dublin.

Glatt took the Swiftian reference, assimilated it and raised the ancient Zeiss glasses to his fevering brow.

'It's a Big Book,' he said, half to himself, 'the Biggest Book of the decade.'

For a civil servant nearing retirement Parkinson was a fast mover. Never mind that others did the moving, they did so at his behest. Car, Board of Trade Lear Jet, and car again. It was faster than a stout tub bumping through choppy brine. But even allowing for the speed of his progress the old man had time for thought and what he thought of was Bognor. He'd known him for years, ever since he'd come to the Board wet behind the ears fresh from university. Wet behind the ears still, yet with a darker grey to the matter between them. In earlier days he would do the wrong thing for the wrong reason – or for no reason at all, which was at least as bad. Nowadays he was more inclined to do the wrong thing for the right reason and this was why Parkinson had himself so impulsively decided to hurry to Byfleet-next-the-Sea. Bognor left to his own devices would almost inevitably end up in some fearful scrape but the reason for that was that his hunches were usually well founded. He got himself into trouble because he knew where the trouble was. If the Board was to get its act together it would use Bognor like a tracker dog, get him to sniff out the enemy and then go in with all reasonable force, hoping not only to apprehend the villain but also – less essential – to get Bognor out safely.

Swooping low over the flat quilt of East Anglia with its irregular squares and oblongs laid out below in contrasting shades of wintry grey, Parkinson was forced to admit that continued use of Bognor in dangerous situations betrayed a callous disregard for the man's life. If he genuinely valued Bognor he would have taken him off Special Operations and put him on desk-bound code and cipher work as he had so often threatened. But he hadn't and the knowledge caused Parkinson a twinge of self-revelation. He did not think of himself as a cruel or a cold man and yet he was forced to acknowledge that sooner or later he was going to be responsible for Bognor's death. Oddly enough what upset him most about that was not the loss of Bognor but the thought of having to explain the circumstances to Monica, Mrs Bognor.

He was still trying to rationalise this when the little plane put down at Norton Fitzpriors, the old RAF base where Strobe's chopper had landed in the middle of the night. The place hadn't seen so much activity since 1940. Shading his eyes against an unexpected shaft of sun he saw an unmarked car in the lee of one of the hangars. Two men leaned against it, their belted macs immediately identifying them as hard men of the intimidatory tendency.

Parkinson rubbed his hands. He had never carried a weapon since the embarrassing business of Bulstrode in Berlin in '48. For the first time in ages the lack had made him feel naked and vulnerable. Which is why he had made the pilot radio Lowestoft and ordered Krichefski and Horowitz to drop their Customs and Excise assignment and get over to meet him p.d.q. With those two around he might not expect razor-sharp conversation but at least he'd feel safe.

Safe was more than Bognor was feeling.

The wind had increased by several knots and the sea heightened by more than a foot. At one point Trevor came down grinning broadly. He put his finger to his lips to indicate silence, made a thumbs-up signal and went away again with a large piece of rope slung over his shoulder. Bognor did not feel encouraged by this. Water was sloshing about in their primitive cabin and his feet were getting soaked. He tried to remember everything he had ever read about displacement and the effect of even a few inches of water on a ship's stability. He could remember nothing.

It was impossible to hear voices. Impossible to hear anything above the sea and the engine. Borrowing Molly's Chinon glasses again, he saw that they were definitely closing on the *Dolores Ibarruri*. The East German ship was indeed festooned with all manner of strange devices. As he watched, Bognor saw an officer on the bridge scanning the sea with binoculars. He had obviously seen them but something else seemed to be engaging his attention. Bognor followed his gaze and focused as hard as he could. No use. He could see nothing. The German, however, could.

Then, as he watched, desperately straining to see through the weather and to remain more or less upright, there was a small eruption from the stern of the *Dolores Ibarruri*, a cotton wool pompom hung in the air, a thin trail of smoke sped upwards and then burst in a bright red star above the boat. Seconds later there was a muffled explosion from above and green smoke came eddying down to sea.

'Very lights,' said Bognor.

Molly smiled and scribbled. 'Named after an American naval officer called Edward Very who died just before the Great War,' she said. 'Ask me another.'

'I'm going to have to stop them,' said Bognor, feeling sicker than ever. 'The bastards are defecting.'

Monica was not sure about the Strobe gang.

That Andover Strobe himself was one of the most successful of the new breed of British publishers was incontestable. No four-flusher he. His attitude to the product was robust, commercial and populist. He understood the business; he had no trace of sentiment; no hint of literary aspiration. He was

165

ambitious – his enemies would say greedy – and he was a capitalist. If he kept on the right side of the law it was because he regarded this as only sensible, not because any moral issues were involved. At the Haven Monica had been impressed by his control. He cut an absurd figure in his spacey wheelchair and his garish outfit but he had authentic menace based on evident self-discipline. Now, however, he seemed to be losing touch with reality.

'Rambo, crambo!' he cried, as the firm's Harrod-green Range Rover creamed towards Byfleet Pier, gears expertly crashed by Hastings. The wheelchair was fastened into the back by a custom-built magnetic locking device which still enabled Strobe to turn it hither and thither in order to get the best possible view. Monica sat on the floor while he kept the gold machine-gun trained on her navel. 'Metal screeches against metal, Mrs Bognor,' he said as Hastings double declutched, 'as if each strip, each panel was fighting to survive the successive impacts of . . . I quote, I paraphrase . . . have you ever noticed how life so often imitates art but so rarely approximates to the prosody of the Megabuster? Do you read me, Mrs Bognor?'

'I think,' said Monica, struggling to maintain her grip on the side of the Range Rover and of reality, 'that prosody means something else.'

'Meaning, schmeaning, Mrs Bognor,' said Strobe. 'What is meaning compared with life?'

The Range Rover took briefly to the pavement, narrowly missed a parked three-wheeler and a slow-moving pram, rose off a couple of wheels, clumped back to four-wheel contact. The tyres squawked. Monica would have done the same but was concerned to keep face. Strobe's chair was obviously equipped with keen stabilisers.

'The Japanese have a word for it,' continued Strobe, ignoring the captive's silence.

If so he was unable to think of it, for he lapsed into introspective quiet.

'Where the hell's the boat?' Hastings skidded the vehicle to a halt.

'Hugh said end of pier.' Glopff had obviously been told to

economise with speech during moments of crisis.

'Do we have a key?'

The pier was bleak and shuttered. Rusting metal gates barred the entrance. They were padlocked.

'Shit, no,' said Glopff. She swung down from the front seat, paced over to the barrier, rattled it, kicked it, returned. 'You'll have to drive through it,' she said.

Monica had noted the Range Rover's reinforced fenders. Now, turning her head she saw peeling paint, last year's fairy lights, a decayed advertisement for afternoon tea dances at the end of the pier and another for Hot Buttered Toast and the Coffee Pots. She just had time to take in that it was orange and yellow with a photograph of a tall Caucasian male and a chorus line of scantily clad Filipino girls when the gears crashed again, Hastings engaged the most powerful he could find, slipped the clutch and charged. Seconds later there was a tearing splinter, a hardly perceptible jolt and the four of them were bowling along Byfleet Pier at around forty.

Andover Strobe, cradling his little gun, began to croon Cole Porter: 'Are you fond of swimming, dear?

       Kindly tell me, if so.

       Yes, I'm fond of swimming, dear,

       But in the morning, no.'

A wave broke beneath the pier and spray dusted the windshield.

Monica shivered.

On the bridge of HMS *Snapdragon* Merlin Glatt and Lieutenant Tregarron both saw the red and green of the two flares. Tregarron made a terse signal to the engine room and ordered his number two to alter course to port. The *Snapdragon*'s head turned into the wind and she dipped into the waves like a prop forward barging in the line-out.

Glatt raised an eyebrow.

'Contact,' he said, 'earlier than I anticipated.'

Tregarron grimaced.

'We're faster than we look, Mr Glatt,' he said.

'We'd better be, Tregarron,' Glatt scowled. 'If those Krauts are away and out of territorial waters before we get there I and my friends are going to be most unhappy.'

Below decks on the *Saucy Sue*, Bognor and Molly Mortimer held a council of war, taking Dutch comfort from the remains of the rum.

'They'll be armed,' said Molly, eyes wide.

'I doubt it. Green is a wimp.'

'But he thinks he's Lance Remington. In which case he's bound to be armed. And we know they have a Very pistol.'

'Even if they're armed they'd never shoot. Not at a person.'

'Romany Flange might, she looks totally ruthless to me. And you think she killed Audrey Hemlock.'

'I do?'

'You do.' Molly flung back rum. 'I read you like a book, Simon. As you well know.'

'Well, you read right this time.'

Bognor wished the boat would stop moving. He looked out of the porthole with the Chinon glasses. The *Dolores Ibarruri* and the *Saucy Sue* were closing fast now. Only about a hundred yards separated them. Bognor could make out the stitching on the cable-knit sweaters of the crew. There were some decidedly thuggish-looking people on board. If he and Molly Mortimer were to make a move they would have to make it fast. As soon as they were in touch with the East Germans they would be outnumbered and outgunned. He wondered if Trevor kept a gun down here swilling around among the sea-water and slops and fishing tackle and string.

'You'll have to bluff,' said Molly.

'Bluff?'

'If you don't have a proper gun you'll just have to pretend.'

'They'll never believe it.'

'You've no alternative. It's either that or they defect, taking the book with them.'

Bognor watched the approaching Germans and pondered. Pondering time was limited. He lifted the glasses and stared at the taffrail. A stocky, rather familiar figure was leaning over the stern being sick over the ship's name. Bognor turned away

168

partly from disgust, partly because he did not wish to intrude into private suffering. His own stomach was registering disturbing symptoms as if in sympathy.

Presently, however, he turned back, not knowing quite why. He was still wrestling with his plans. Was he about to go on deck and indulge in dangerous heroics? Or was he going to stay here and play safe? Left to his own devices he would have kept quiet but the presence of a woman, particularly a woman such as Molly Mortimer, did have a certain galvanising quality. He retrained his glasses on the sick person in the stern of the Rostock fishing boat. As he did he let out a little yelp of recognition.

'Good grief!' he exclaimed. 'Dr Belgrave!'

Parkinson was too late to see the Very lights which were, in any case, too far out to sea to be visible to the naked eye.

A quick courtesy call on the car radio to Bumstead told Bognor's boss what he suspected. Bumstead was interrogating Milton Capstick and Danvers Warrington and showed every sign of charging one or other or possibly both with the murder of Vernon and Audrey Hemlock. Warrington had admitted being Audrey's lover and the DCI seemed to regard this as conclusive evidence of the wine buff's unreliability. Capstick was clearly being bothersome and it sounded ominously as if Bumstead was going to charge him with obstructing the course of justice, pending something more serious.

When Parkinson asked him if he had any clue about where the Bognors were Bumstead replied that they were 'off his patch' and that he had given Bognor 'a flea in his ear'. Parkinson swore under his breath and remarked out loud that he supposed Bognor would therefore be 'sick as a parrot'. Bumstead concurred, having, evidently, no ear for irony.

'What about Strobe, Glopff and the butler?' asked the Board of Trade mandarin.

'Hot on their trail,' replied the policeman. 'I anticipate an arrest in the nearest possible future but at this moment in time I am not at liberty to divulge their precise whereabouts.'

This time Parkinson could not forbear to swear out loud. He

did so noisily and very profanely, causing Krichefski and Horowitz to exchange amused and irreverent glances.

A quick visit to the Goose and Goblet however led them immediately to the harbour where in the snug of the Mermaid's Tail the Board of Trade men swiftly established from a hirsute, peg-legged regular that the *Saucy Sue* had put to sea with a highly irregular human cargo. Parkinson briefly considered going in hot pursuit but thought better of it when he contemplated the choppy waters and even more so when the disabled salt vouchsafed the further information that a Harrod-green Range Rover had recently passed by at a rate of knots. Parkinson remembered that his wife's collection of *Great Romances of the Universe*, published by the firm of Andover Strobe, was uniformly wrapped in what was described in the firm's advertising literature as 'the distinctive and prestigious olive livery of the world's greatest publishing house'. Jamming his Homburg back on his head he made for the door. Moments later, at the pier, Krichefski let out a shout and pointed to the broken gates jangling in the gale. Horowitz swung the car into a screeching ninety-degree turn, grazed the jagged edges of metalwork and bombed towards the pierhead.

The Battle of Byfleet was about to begin.

Bognor had intended to approach with cat-like tread, taking his quarry unawares. The rising storm confounded this intention. One minute he was standing at the top of the companion way, clasping the little Chinon binoculars in the right-hand pocket of his Barbour where he and Molly Mortimer had convinced themselves that its snubby double barrel could do duty as a disguised Board of Trade special issue firearm – the next he was catapulted by a heavy wave, through the doors onto the deck, issuing forth with all the menace of a newly landed monster from the deep. As he crashed, he screamed.

The sound was inarticulate but – even above the weather – audible. It was also alarming.

Trevor was in the wheelhouse but Arthur Green and Romany Flange were both on deck holding on to the side of the vessel and staring across at the approaching *Dolores Ibarruri*. Hurtling

170

through the door Bognor came to a stop some six feet from the pair of them. His right hand still clasped the gun-like shape in his macintosh pocket and despite a stagger and gasp he stayed upright. The spectacle of a stoutish, fortyish, middle-aged man, green of face and green of coat, pretending to be on the verge of serious shooty-bangs on the high seas might under normal circumstances have seemed preposterous or even laughable. But to Arthur and Romany, steeped in the fantasy world of Big Books, the sudden menace was authentic, even predictable. Others less professionally suggestible might have wondered why if Bognor had a gun, he was hiding it in his pocket. It was what one did in the street, certainly, but here, on the ocean wave?

They froze.

Bognor also had a spasm of silent indecision but was rescued by Molly Mortimer. She had been right behind him as he crashed through the doors and now she went swiftly to his side clutching a dirty crowbar she had picked up downstairs.

'Do exactly as Mr Bognor says,' she said. 'The gun is loaded and if I know him he won't hesitate to use it.'

She turned to the wheelhouse. 'Trevor,' she called, 'our time is up! Back to port!'

The German ship was closing fast.

Bognor collected his thoughts. 'Frankly,' he said, 'Her Majesty's Board of Trade doesn't care very much what happens to you two, but we're not keen on the papers you're carrying getting to Moscow – or even Rostock.' He pointed at the expandable lightweight sac at Green's feet. 'Hand that over now. And no silly stuff.'

Green bent down to pick it up. But even as he did so there was a sharp report from the *Dolores Ibarruri*, a coil of rope snaked across the water and a vicious barbed harpoon embedded itself firmly in the decking a couple of feet to their starboard.

'Breeches-buoy,' shouted Trevor. 'Boarding party!'

Bognor looked across at the enemy and saw that a group of men in woolly hats and white polo necks were doing intricate things with the rope at their end. One of them pointed his arms in their direction, there was a stab of fire, a staccato crackle and a flight of lead whined high above them through the rigging of

171

the *Saucy Sue*. Another figure on the bridge of the 'fishing boat' addressed them through a sophisticated-looking megaphone. He did so in heavily accented language-school English and the sentiments were very similar to those expressed by the Literary Editor of the *Globe* to the publisher and her author.

'Hello, Herr Bognor! We know you are on board. You are please advised not to trouble making be. We are aboard coming and we would like not to shooting with the weapons.'

'Krautspeaking schweinhund!' snapped Bognor, wondering if Captain W. E. Johns would have been a Big Book author or a Strobe man, 'Trevor, can you cut that rope?'

'Not bloody likely, mate,' shouted Trevor. 'No way I'm going to be aereated by a Commie goon with a high-speed shooter, know what I mean?'

There was shooting on the pier as well.

Halfway down, between Terry's Jellied Eels and Frankie's Fries, there was a double burst from either side of the Mozzarella Marine Ices kiosk. One took the offside front tyre and the other accounted for most of the windscreen, neatly bisecting the passengers and doing nothing worse than shower them with glass.

Horowitz braked hard, skidded left and ended up sideways on to Gypsy Romano's Fortune Telling Booth, Est. 1873, 'The Future *is* Yours to Sea, to Sea'. The three of them piled out and hit the deck in the prescribed Board of Trade Special Investigations Department Training Manual style.

'Armed publishers,' said Parkinson, bitterly, 'in this day and age, in Great Britain. It makes a mockery of everything I've tried to do in my career. Pen mightier than sword, rational civilised debate, intelligent communications between consenting adults, liberal consensus, tea and sandwiches at Number Ten, good God – is this what the world's come to?'

He raised his head and shouted towards the pierhead. 'Strobe, we know you're there, now for God's sake come out like a rational human being and stop these ludicrous games. I'll count to ten then I want you to wheel yourself out with your hands above your head. One . . . two . . . three . . .'

On the count of five there was a shout which sounded like

'Banzai!', an object the size of a cricket ball sailed high to their left, bounced on some railings, ricocheted on the scaffolding below and behind them and exploded with a dull crump. A hole appeared in the surface of the pier and the firework smell of cordite hung in the air.

'Ah well,' said Parkinson, 'at least that may attract some sort of attention.'

It was nothing as elaborate as a breeches-buoy, just a sort of hook to keep the invaders from falling into the sea. As Bognor watched, a burly bloke pushed off from the *Dolores Ibarruri* and started to make his way towards them. He had a rifle strapped to his back and a knife in his teeth. The knife was a dramatic gesture but not helpful since it presumably deprived him of the power of speech. Perhaps he did not speak English.

Bognor had an idea.

He passed Green's case to Molly Mortimer. 'See if you can find the Butskell-Godunov stuff,' he said. She took the case and started to rummage. Looking across to the enemy ship Bognor saw that despite the choppiness and the heaving of the two boats Fritz was making surprisingly fast progress. Worse still, a couple of other Fritzes had swung out onto the rope behind him. Bognor called across to the leader of the advancing assault group.

'Achtung! Achtung!' he shouted. 'Ich bin Simon Bognor von der Britisher Board of Trade. Halt!'

To his considerable satisfaction he observed a definite pause in their progress. It was a brief pause, true, but they obviously recognised the voice of authority.

'Ich have "*Halt*" er . . . gesagen,' he bawled, *Halt!*'

This time the pause was briefer.

'Got it,' said Molly, with an air of triumph. She produced what looked like a barrister's brief – a great stack of foolscap tied together with pink ribbon. Also two five-and-a-half-inch floppy disks. 'The disks say "First Lady",' she said.

'Great,' said Bognor. 'Just hold them up so these chaps can see them and then if anyone makes a false move throw them overboard.' He now turned his attentions to the interlopers. 'Now listen to me, you men!' he bawled. 'These papers which my colleague has in her possession, these are the papers which your masters are after. If you allow these papers to fall into the sea your masters will be displeased. If I know anything about your part of the world they will have you taken out and shot. Bang bang, you're dead!'

He paused, pleased to note that they too had paused again. But the pause was his undoing. By facing out to sea he had removed his attention from Green and Flange. By holding up the Butskell-Godunov papers Molly had been forced to lay down her crowbar. Thus they were vulnerable. Also the sight of his Biggest Book and its source material about to go overboard and be lost to himself and to posterity aroused all the dormant Lance Remington in the wimpish author.

Arthur Green launched himself on Simon Bognor.

Romany Flange thrust herself at Molly Mortimer.

The four of them went down in a heap.

The mêlée lasted only a moment and was predictably inconclusive. Bognor had copped out of the last Board of Trade Refresher Course in Unarmed Combat run by ex-Sergeant-Major McKillop of the Scots Guards. Unarmed Combat had never been one of his skills, anyway. Nor Arthur Green's. The women were more formidable but their long dangerous nails and their long clutchable hair cancelled themselves out. Oddly, the only casualty was Captain Trevor who decided he had better join in, tripped over an ill-coiled rope by the door of the wheelhouse, slipped and fell, hitting his head on the corner of a lobster pot which knocked him out cold.

This shocked the other four but not as much as the fate of the papers. The two disks got swept into a gutter of bilgewater which must have rendered them useless, though someone as efficient as Green would, Bognor presumed, have made back-up disks. But the papers, the precious papers, lost their pink binding and started to flutter hither and yon. As soon as this happened all four protagonists forgot their enmity and started trying to gather them up, but the harder they tried the more they fell about and bumped into each other, and the more scattered and bedraggled and lost the papers became.

In the few seconds that this fracas lasted, the men from the

Dolores Ibarruri made no further progress but stayed swaying on their ropes watching for the outcome, hypnotised by the oddity of the encounter. Then, just when they might have been on the move again, there was a sound of further gunfire. This was a different gunfire – not the ratatatat of kettle-drum machine-gun fire but the more sonorous boom of something heavier. An old three- or four-inch gun, Bognor guessed. And then a shell splashed into the water ahead of the *Dolores Ibarruri* and there was an underwater explosion. It was all oddly like an old black-and-white war movie except that the monochrome sea and spray made it real and frightening. There was another boom and another splash and this time the shell fell astern so that the *Dolores Ibarruri* was bracketed and the men swaying on their ropes hesitated for a moment, and then a figure appeared on the bridge in a cap with gold braid and he shouted out words in German of which Bognor could just catch '*Achtung!*' and '*Schnell!*' and the men started to positively scamper back to their ship, hand over hand.

'The cavalry!' said Bognor. He took the binoculars out of his pocket, ignored the furious expressions on the faces of Flange and Green, scanned the horizon, and found the squat, grey features of HMS *Snapdragon* bearing down on them from the south-east.

'Royal Navy,' he said, with an air of authority, as the German boat cast off the harpoon line and let it splash into the sea. Bognor switched his gaze back to the *Dolores Ibarruri*. There was much activity. The captain, if captain it was, was looking thunderous on the bridge. Astern, Bognor saw Dr Belgrave, seemingly recovered from her sea-sickness. She too had a pair of field-glasses and was studying the *Saucy Sue* as intently as Bognor was studying the fishing boat from Rostock. Bognor screwed his eyes up to the lens and concentrated extra hard. There was no mistaking her. She was the same person that had poured out her life story only yesterday in the Marine Ice Cream Parlour on the front at Byfleet-next-the-Sea.

Seeing him watch her, the Doctor lowered her glasses and waved, twice slowly. Then as the *Dolores Ibarruri* turned away and gathered pace, she blew a kiss. Bognor, mystified, blew one back.

Molly Mortimer looked at him oddly. 'What on earth are you doing?' she asked.

Bognor thought for a moment and decided that she had quite enough of a story for her paper already.

'Just waving and smiling,' he said. 'It's what one does when one's feeling a bit smug and superior but not quite sure why. Read the latest *Royal Family Bedside Book* and you'll see what I mean.'

The *Saucy Sue* lurched and shipped a cold douche of wave. The skipper stirred on the deck but did not wake.

'OK, superman,' said Molly Mortimer, 'now perhaps you'll take us all back to port.'

Bognor, who couldn't tell a sheepshank from a round turn and two half-hitches, had no idea how to scandalise the yards, and thought a binnacle was another name for a barnacle, was not the man to take the *Saucy Sue* and her passengers home through the storms and currents of Byfleet Bay. Such a man, however, was near at hand and such a man, of course, was Glatt. Glatt, starved of real action, longing to have boarded the *Dolores Ibarruri* and to have performed some man-to-man heroics possibly involving the use or at least the threat of his Navajo knife, was delighted to be able to climb aboard the *Saucy Sue* using the same Tarzan technique as the East Germans.

If he was discomfited by Bognor's presence on board he did not admit it, indeed took mild satisfaction from Simon's obvious lack of real mannishness. He was more put out to find Molly Mortimer, not because she was 'press' but because she had apparently been patronising about last year's *Collected Glatt*. 'A fearful case of *de haut en bas*,' he said, 'and God knows what in the world you have to be patronising about.'

Molly, knowing that she had the most tremendous scoop, was in no mood for such gripes. 'You were very lucky to be reviewed at all,' she said, as Glatt spun the wheel with one hand, 'and if you're not careful I shall be perfectly beastly about *The Bestiary*.'

'I never read reviews anyway,' said Glatt, 'but one's relations become easily upset. I have aunts who read the *Globe*.'

As they neared the shore all six – including the reviving Trevor – were aware of a commotion around the pier. Puffs of smoke, crackles and bangs, a highly amplified voice hectoring . . .

'Aha!' said Glatt. 'Could this be the rest of the American contingent? The Strobe faction? Our people apprehended a Jetfoil earlier which was on its way to an RV somewhere or other we couldn't quite make out.'

Bognor seldom thought of himself as psychic but suddenly he felt a stomach churning which had nothing to do with wind or weather.

'My God!' he said. 'I have a hideous feeling my wife may have missed her train.'

It had been a bad few hours for Monica, Mrs Bognor.

Ugly moment the first was when no transport materialised at the pierhead.

Ugly moment the second was when Parkinson's car came steaming towards them blocking the only exit.

The only way out was by sea.

Strobe's eyes were like dairy delight Catherine wheels; Hastings seemed dangerously taut; only Marlene Glopff retained the high-gloss cool of the true professional.

'Six thirty-three in Langley,' she said, glancing at her watch. 'Bad time. It's when they change shifts. Any case, my guess is that they've written us off. Deny all knowledge, dammit.'

'They can't do that,' said Strobe.

'Sure can,' said Marlene, flexing a pectoral.

'You mean the boat's not coming?' said Hastings.

'I mean just that.'

Glopff and Hastings took up positions either side of the ice cream kiosk and exchanged occasional desultory fire with the police sharpshooters who had arrived soon after the grenade went off. Bumstead had taken control of the operation, immediately banishing Parkinson and his team to the front and maintaining a bombastic harangue through his loudspeaker. Strobe and Monica remained in the kiosk. They had run out of conversation.

After a while Glopff came in. 'Our hostage is the only chance,' she said, glancing malice at Monica. 'She has to work for us. Otherwise we might as well kill her right now.'

'How?' asked Strobe, fingering the trigger of his gun.

Glopff bent low over the wheelchair and whispered.

Presently Strobe began to smile.

Not a pretty sight.

Both Glatt and Bognor scanned the pier with their binoculars. Trevor, miraculously restored, was at the wheel.

'Good heavens,' said Merlin Glatt, presently, 'I do believe I see your wife.'

'You what?' Bognor felt worse than ever. Glatt's glasses were more powerful than his.

'Do you see that sleeping-bag shape hanging from the boom? About six feet above sea level.'

Bognor saw what he meant. The little Chinon glasses showed no more than a canvas body bag, blurred at this range, swinging to and fro above the waves that broke against the extremity of the pier.

Glatt handed Bognor his Zeiss glasses without a word.

It was true. The Strobe gang had hung what did indeed look like an army surplus sleeping bag from a boom which protruded from the pier. The draw string was pulled quite tight at the top. It did not, for the most part, look like a body except that at the top there was a human head, white, drawn, still alive and, magnified through the glasses, unmistakably his Monica's.

'Jesus!' said Bognor.

'Swine!' said Glatt, nostrils flared, the fine line of high cheekbone tight against the skin. His mouth was set in a thin line. 'She's their only hope. One false move by that oaf Bumstead and they'll cut that rope and let her drown.'

It was true. A dud grenade with a paper stuck to it had announced the fact to the besieging policemen not five minutes before. If safe passage was not arranged within the hour Monica would be cut from her gibbet and sent to a watery grave. Any attempt to storm the ice cream kiosk and then, too, Marlene or

Hastings would cut the rope which was all that now bound Mrs Bognor to this earth.

There was a strange glint in the poet's eye.

'War, war is still the cry,' he murmured, 'war even to the knife.' He looked back to the skipper. 'Full steam ahead, Trevor, and swing round as close as you dare.' Saying which he pulled the Navajo knife from his boot and pressed the razor-sharp metal to his thumb so that a little trickle of blood oozed out. 'Faith with the blade,' he said, in Gurkhali.

It did not go entirely according to plan. The *Saucy Sue* was a cumbersome tub; Trevor was exhausted and not entirely competent at the best of times; it was still rough, even in these relatively sheltered waters. As they neared the end of the pier Trevor brought the bows round so that Glatt standing at the very edge of the deck was almost directly under the body bag. An amazing leap, worthy of the line-out jumper he had once been, a flash of the snickersnee and the rope was severed.

With terrifying speed Bognor's wife fell through the air and into the waiting arms of her husband and the author Green.

She was alive.

'Darling!' she said.

'Hello!' he said.

And then, as Trevor went about, the side of the *Saucy Sue* was caught by a strong wave. The *Saucy Sue* though old and ugly was strong and serviceable. Byfleet Pier was old and ugly too, but not as strong.

There was a splintering crash. The old timbers cracked, buckled, started to collapse. Trevor revved and revved. The little boat tugged away from the ailing pier. And slowly, slowly, that pride of the Edwardian seaside began to give way and slide with a heartstopping inexorability into the angry waters of the bay. The *Saucy Sue* was not twenty yards away but moving as fast as wind and current would allow when there was a massive explosion. And another. And another.

When the smoke cleared, Mr Mozzarella's ice cream kiosk was no more. Nor the end of the pier. Nor Andover Strobe. Nor Marlene Glopff. Nor even the butler.

The only sign that they had been there was a state-of-the-art wheelchair, bobbing in the briny, borne up on its self-inflating, supposedly life-saving buoyancy tanks.

But empty.

EIGHT

'I don't fancy a long post-mortem,' said Monica, sipping vintage Clicquot at Boris, their new favourite restaurant, very very much later. They had both undergone hours of exceedingly tiresome debrief from Five, Six, BOT (SID), the Cabinet Office, Parkinson, Bumstead, Glatt and others too numerous to mention.

'You know, of course, that poor Audrey wans't murdered, after all.' Bognor sipped too and signalled to the waiter for another half. 'People like Bumstead and even Glatt are so ready to jump to obvious conclusions. Their imaginations get over-heated. They can't admit the possibility of accidental death, coincidence, the everyday currency of everyday life. Everything has to be murder and conspiracy and things that go bump in the night. If only they'd bothered to wait for the post-mortem and ask a few intelligent questions.'

'What happened?'

'Heart attack. She'd obviously had a steamy night with old Warrington – as suggested by the strand of yellow stocking. Must have been, let's say, excited, by Hemlock's death. Then Romany came in and started creating hell and the whole thing was too much for the ticker. Hardly surprising. How are you feeling, by the way?'

'Tired.' Monica put out a hand and stroked her husband's frayed cuff. 'And Hemlock himself?'

'Ah,' said Bognor, 'there you have me. And them. Motives everywhere and not a bit of proof. But that's publishing, I suppose. Let's go and eat.'

A week later a letter with a Cyrillic script postmark arrived chez Bognor.

'Dear Simon (if I may),
    A word of apology. It was smart of Glatt to insert my

obit. in *The Times*, *Telegraph*, etc. – though I could tell that clever Massingberd boy smelt a rat. I was sorry to see "Daisy's Diary" scattered on the ocean deep. All my own work as you must have guessed by now and I'm sorry I pretended otherwise. Dear Daisy was far too scatter-brained to keep a proper diary so it seemed reasonable to invent one. And I'm glad your friend Miss Mortimer was able to spin such a yarn from the whole saga. On the other hand I was sorry to have to deceive you. You have such a nice trusting face. Far too nice to be doing the job you do!

'You presumably realise that I was responsible for squashing poor Vernon in the basement. Nothing particularly personal but my control here in Moscow had decided it was time for me to get things moving and killing Vernon seemed an agreeably dramatic way to set about it. My masters thought that you, Glatt and possibly A. N. Other had rumbled me and it was time to pull me in. Now I'm not so sure.

'I was amused too to read the Literary Editor's exclusive in the *Globe*. "D" Notices and Official Secrets Act invoked, I assume? It made tremendously funny reading but I don't imagine many of her readers could have made head or tail of it. "Publisher perishes in end of pier show!" Honestly! My regular British press reading is now confined to the *Guardian Weekly* and I can't say I miss the tabloids. On the other hand it must be said that *Pravda* lacks a certain dash!

'Quite apart from not getting Daisy's diary out I was sorry about the other side of the swap. Presumably your interrogators have done a proper job on Flange and Green. Such a greedy girl! She fell for the Gorbachev File hook, line and sinker. Him being Anastasia's illegitimate grandson, Andropov alive and rather unwell in a Siberian psychiatric ward, the wife's little dalliance with George Schultz . . . the lot. If you're interested in trading something else do let me know. The Bishop of Durham perhaps?

182

'If you're ever this way do spend a weekend at the dacha. Kim will give you directions. Or young Martin W. Such a bright boy!

'You must admit the people on this side of the curtain have a much more vivid imagination than the West credits them with. Mama always said so and even if she was scatty she was blessed with insights not vouchsafed to the rest of us.

'In a Big Book I suppose I'd have been called a sleeper but I always felt so wide awake. Enjoyed every moment of it. Making trouble is so agreeable, don't you think, and with the Bumsteads of this world ever with us, so terribly easy. Don't you think?

'Take care. And if you ever feel like a change of scenery you know what to do.

'Yours ever,
Ann Belgrave (née Butskell-Godunov)'

Six months later Parkinson passed over a trade paper clipping:

'The Trustees of the Flange Institution have announced the most valuable Literary Prize yet. The £50,000 annual Hemlock–Strobe Award in memory of Britain's biggest publishers is to go to the Biggest Book of the Year. The judges are Miss Romany Flange; the poet Mr Merlin Glatt; the novelist Mr Arthur Green; and the biographer Miss Miranda Howard.'

Underneath, Parkinson had scrawled, 'Am prepared to nominate your history of the Board's Special Investigations Department. Should I live so long. Yrs P.'

Bognor barged straight in through his chief's famous open door.

'Dammit,' he said, tight-lipped. 'It's not a joking matter. Flange and Green are as traitorous as Burgess and Maclean. They should be put on trial. If they're not I shall reveal all to Chapman Pincher. I'll go to Australia and find a publisher.'

Parkinson shook his head sadly.

'We don't hang, draw and quarter any more, dear boy,' he said. 'Traitor's Gate's a tourist attraction – or hadn't you noticed? We've got a lot more sophisticated now. The minute

183

we discover a traitor in our midst we load them with honours and laud them with praise. It's policy. Ever since that old queen who looked after the Queen's pictures.'

Bognor shook his head, disbelief battling with rage. 'You people,' he said, 'would have given Judas a life peerage and made Lord Haw-Haw President of the MCC.'

Parkinson nodded. 'Probably,' he said. 'It's called Blunt's Law.'